Contents

SANDWICH GRILLS AND WAFFLE BAKERS

SPACE HEATERS

Section II: General Repair Procedures

Preface

Modern technology has surrounded woman with a vast assortment of electrical appliances. These are the tools she has grown to depend upon to help her perform household laundry, cooking, and cleaning chores. She has become expert in their use, but she has been too long denied the knowledge of what to do when they malfunction.

Women's patience and manual dexterity will help them effectively to use this book. It deals directly with the most frequently encountered problems in small heat-producing electrical appliances. It provides the practical "know-how" needed to restore operation to and to prolong the useful life of appliances, in easy-to-follow, step-by-step instructions. Each repair can mean substantial dollar savings. Equally important, this book will serve as a guide for determining when the services of professional repair technicians are required.

Line drawings are used abundantly throughout the book because they are usually better visual aids than photographs. The appliances used as models for illustrations were chosen because they incorporate the design features most often found in popular brands.

The repair procedures outlined in each *problem solver* are arranged in simple, short steps. Each *problem solver* should be read through completely to establish continuity before beginning any adjustment or repair. Naturally, any appliance being worked on should be unplugged. Extreme care has been exercised to make sure that the person attempting repairs will encounter no danger of injury. All repairs are simple and easily made. Any complex repairs or those involving any possible risk clearly must be referred to the attention of a qualified repair technician.

In many instances the author suggests the use of common household tools and materials to accomplish the adjustment or repair of an appliance. A glossary is included to introduce and illustrate less familiar tools.

Section I

Repair Problems and
Their Solutions

Problem Solver #1

APPLIANCE: Clothes Irons (Steam and Regular)

PROBLEM: **Iron does not slide smoothly over cloth.**

EXPLANATION: There are two conditions that most often cause an iron to snag and pull. One is caused by foreign material that has burned and hardened on the sole plate of the iron. The second is caused by small burrs (often difficult to see or feel) that have been scratched out of the soft aluminum sole plate.

TOOLS AND MATERIALS NEEDED:

(a) a small block of wood or small empty plastic box

(b) a piece of fine grit sandpaper or emery cloth

(c) fine-texture steel wool pad or an abrasive type plastic cleaning pad

(d) scouring cleanser powder (used for sinks, etc.)

SOLUTION: 1. Wrap sandpaper (or emery cloth) around the sanding block (wood or plastic box). (*Figure 1*)

2. Hold iron in upright position and rub sanding block against the sole plate with a straight up and down movement. Keep the sanding block flat against the sole plate, and use only moderate pressure. (*Figure 2*)

3. Continue to sand the sole plate until all burned-on residue and deep scratches have been removed. Be sure not to overlook any nicks along the edges of the sole plate.

NOTE: Use a fresh piece of sandpaper as often as necessary.

4. Sanding is properly completed when the sole plate takes on an even, dull appearance.

FIG.1

SANDING BLOCK

SANDPAPER

FIG.2

SOLE PLATE

5. Form steel wool into a pad and place it under the sanding block. (*Figure 3*)

6. Rub the steel wool in an up and down motion against the sole plate until a fine satin finish is obtained.

7. Thoroughly dampen a soft piece of cloth with water and fold it to form a pad the size of the sanding block and about ½ inch in thickness. Place the pad on the sanding block.

8. Sprinkle scouring cleanser on the damp pad and allow cleanser to absorb some of the moisture from the pad to form a thick paste.

9. Polish the sole plate with the cleanser paste until it takes on a bright sheen.

   CAUTION: If you are working on a steam iron, remove any cleanser paste that may have accumulated in the steam ports of the sole plate with the end of a paper clip or hairpin. (*Figure 4*)

10. Wipe the sole plate with a clean damp cloth to remove the scouring cleanser.

    CAUTION: To avoid damaging the sole plate of the iron, never allow sharp objects or hard, rough surfaces to come in contact with the sole plate. Always rest and store your iron on its heel.

FIG.3

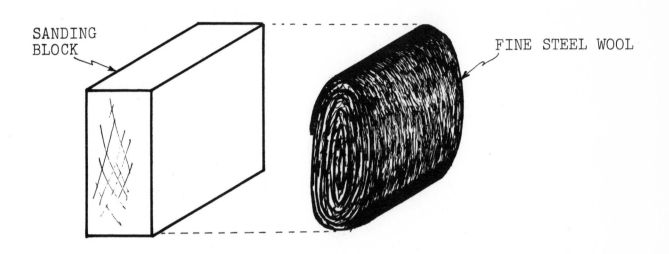

SANDING BLOCK

FINE STEEL WOOL

FIG.4

STEAM PORTS

PAPER CLIP OR HAIRPIN

Problem Solver #2

APPLIANCE: Clothes Irons (Steam Only)

PROBLEM: Not enough steam comes from the iron.

EXPLANATION: Minerals contained in water form hard deposits in the steam chamber and steam ports and can clog the steam passages.

TOOLS AND MATERIALS NEEDED:

    (a) a paper clip or hairpin

    (b) liquid measuring cup

    (c) ½ cup of white vinegar

SOLUTION:

1. Clean the steam ports located in the sole plate with a paper clip or a hairpin bent into shape as illustrated. (*Figure 1*) Wiggle paper clip or hairpin in the steam ports to loosen hardened mineral deposits.

2. Mix a cleaning solution consisting of ½ cup of white vinegar with ½ cup of water. Fill the iron with the vinegar-water solution. (*Figure 2*)

3. Set the fabric indicator dial to the "steam" setting and allow all of the cleaning solution to steam through the iron. Repeat cleaning with vinegar solution if necessary. (*Figure 3*)

    NOTE: Iron may be used immediately after cleaning.

FIG.1

BENT PAPER CLIP
OR HAIRPIN

SOLE PLATE

FIG.2

½
WATER
½
VINEGAR

FIG.3

ALL STEAM PORTS OPEN

Problem Solver #3

APPLIANCE: Clothes Irons (Steam Only)

PROBLEM: **Water and steam sputters out of steam ports during operation.**

EXPLANATION: This condition is caused by an overheated iron. There are two reasons why an iron becomes overheated. The first may simply be an incorrect dial setting. The second may be caused when the thermostat, which automatically controls the temperature of the iron, does not function correctly.

TOOLS AND MATERIALS NEEDED:

    (a) a small screwdriver (sewing machine type)

    (b) a paper clip

    (c) a pair of pliers

SOLUTION: 1. Make certain fabric indicator dial is set correctly to "steam" position.

    2. If water and steam continue to sputter from steam ports with fabric dial correctly set to steam, the thermostat must be checked and adjusted.

    CAUTION: Remove plug from electric outlet and allow iron to cool to room temperature before proceeding.

    SPECIAL NOTE: *Figures 1 and 2* illustrate two of the more widely used types of steam irons. Moreover, they are designed so that the thermostat adjustment screw can be reached easily. The design of other types of irons requires a more complicated disassembly procedure and should therefore be taken to a qualified appliance repair shop for service.

FIG.1

STEAM CONTROL
BUTTON

FABRIC
DIAL

OFF
STEAM

SADDLE
PLATE

FIG.2

CAP RIVET

STEAM CONTROL
KNOB

FABRIC
DIAL
KNOB

3. To reach the thermostat adjustment screw for the type of iron shown in *Figure 1,* gently pry the metal saddle plate off by grasping and lifting both sides with the fingertips. A stubborn saddle plate may be removed by carefully prying one side up with the blade of a screwdriver. (*Figure 3*)

   CAUTION: When using a screwdriver, take care not to pry against the plastic portion of the iron handle located directly below the saddle plate.

4. With saddle plate removed, locate the slotted thermostat adjustment screw. (*Figure 4*)

5. Insert screwdriver blade into the thermostat adjustment screw slot and give the adjustment screw a quarter turn in a clockwise direction.

6. Retest the steam operation of the iron. If the sputtering condition has been improved but some sputtering still exists, give the adjustment screw an additional quarter turn clockwise. Repeat the adjustment once more if necessary.

   NOTE: If adjustment does not correct the sputtering condition, it means that the thermostat is defective and must, therefore, be replaced. Refer such repairs to a qualified appliance service shop.

7. For the final test, shut the iron off and allow it to cool to room temperature. When the iron has thoroughly cooled, set the fabric dial to the lowest heat position (usually "synthetics"). Plug iron into wall receptacle. If iron heats up, adjustment is complete, and the malfunction has been corrected. However, if iron does *not* heat on lowest setting, it means that the thermostat did not respond to the adjustment and is, therefore, defective. Such a defective thermostat must be replaced.

FIG.3

SADDLE PLATE
(BEING REMOVED)

FIG.4

THERMOSTAT
ADJUSTMENT
SCREW

SADDLE PLATE
(REMOVED)

8. To reach the thermostat adjustment screw for the type of iron shown in *Figure 2*, bend a paper clip as shown in *Figure 5*. Place the tip of the paper clip in the center of the plastic cap rivet located on the iron handle and press firmly down until the rivet is pushed clear through into the handle.

9. Grasp the front cap of the iron handle and pull it forward. Disconnect the steam control lever from the top of the valve shaft and remove the front cap. (*Figure 6*)

   CAUTION: Retrieve the cap rivet, which will be found in a little well directly below its position in the handle. Set it aside carefully so that it may be reinstalled after the thermostat adjustment has been completed.

10. Unscrew the valve nut (turn counter-clockwise) with pliers and remove it. Lift off the washer and the thermostat control cam. (*Figure 6*)

PAPER CLIP

FIG.5

STEAM CONTROL LEVER

CAP RIVET

FRONT CAP

CAP RIVET (REMOVED)

STEAM VALVE SHAFT

FIG.6

STEAM CONTROL LEVER

THERMOSTAT CONTROL CAM

VALVE NUT

11. Locate the thermostat adjustment nut. (*Figure 7*) Grasp the adjustment nut with fingers and give it a half turn in a clockwise direction. If nut is stubborn, grasp nut with pliers to turn it. Use only moderate pressure.

12. Replace the thermostat control cam, washer, and valve nut. Tighten valve nut securely with pliers. (*Figure 6*) Connect the steam control lever to the top of the valve shaft and slide the front cap into place. Install the cam rivet. Press rivet firmly into place with the flat side of the pliers.

13. Retest the steam operation of the iron. Repeat thermostat adjustments if necessary (half clockwise turns at a time) until iron steams properly. If adjustments fail to correct sputtering condition, thermostat is defective and should be replaced by a qualified appliance technician.

14. For final test, allow iron to cool to room temperature. Then set fabric dial to the lowest heat position (synthetics). Plug the iron into the wall receptacle. If iron heats up, adjustment is complete and condition has been corrected. If, however, the iron does *not* heat on the lowest setting, it means that the thermostat did not respond to the adjustment and is, therefore, defective and must be replaced.

FIG.7   EXPLODED VIEW

VALVE NUT

THERMOSTAT CONTROL CAM

STEAM VALVE
SHAFT

THERMOSTAT ADJUSTMENT NUT

Problem Solver #4

APPLIANCE: Clothes Irons (Steam and Regular)

PROBLEM: Iron does not heat.

EXPLANATION: Heat is produced in an iron by the effect of an electric current passing through an internal heating element wire. Anything that prevents the electric current from reaching the heating element wire or from passing completely through it will prevent the iron from heating. Most often, the flow of electricity is stopped either when a fuse is blown or when the wires in the iron line cord break due to the flexing, bending, and tugging strain that occurs during normal use.

TOOLS AND MATERIALS NEEDED:

(a) asbestos- and cloth-covered line cord (can be purchased completely assembled with plug and terminal connectors)

(b) a small screwdriver (sewing machine type)

(c) a pair of pliers

SOLUTION:

1. Make certain that the wall outlet has electric power. Plug a lamp or other appliance known to be in good working order into the outlet used for the iron. If lamp or other appliance also fails to operate, it can be assumed that a fuse has blown or that a circuit breaker has tripped "off," thus preventing electric power from reaching the wall outlet, or that the wall receptacle itself is faulty. Refer to Section II, General Repair Procedures, Fuses and Circuit Breakers, for further information about this condition. If, however, the lamp or other appliances operates, it means that the problem is in the iron.

2. Examine the line cord plug. Check the plug prongs for looseness. Test the condition of the line cord wires going into the plug by tugging firmly on the plug against the line cord. (*Figure 1*) If the plug prongs wiggle freely or if the plug seems to part from the line cord when pulled, the plug should be replaced. See Section II, General Repair Procedures, Plugs, for further information.

FIG.1

TERMINAL
COVER
PLATE

POINT WHERE WIRES
OFTEN BREAK

LINE CORD
SLEEVE

LINE CORD

POINT WHERE WIRES
OFTEN BREAK

PLUG
PRONGS

SPECIAL NOTE: While it is possible for wires to break anywhere along the length of the line cord, they are most apt to break at points where sharp bending occurs during use. These points are located where the line cord enters the plug and again where it enters the line cord sleeve. When you are uncertain about breakage or whenever the line cord shows outward signs of wear, such as fraying, replace the entire line cord as outlined in the steps that follow.

CAUTION: Remove line cord from wall outlet before working on iron.

3. Remove the terminal cover plate screw by turning it counter-clockwise with a small screwdriver. (*Figure 2*)

4. Insert the flat tip of the screwdriver along the edge of the terminal cover plate and *gently* pry it out. (*Figure 3*)

5. Examine the line cord wires going to the terminal posts. (*Figure 3*) If wires are attached with push-on connectors, simply grasp each connector with fingertips and pull upwards with a slight side-to-side motion and remove them. (*Figure 3*)

CAUTION: Use moderate pressure to avoid bending or otherwise damaging the terminal posts.

6. If wires are attached with terminal screws, loosen the two screws by giving them two full turns counter-clockwise. (*Figure 4*)

7. Remove the line cord wire ends.

NOTE AND CAUTION: If the line cord wire ends under the screws have U-shaped connectors, the wire ends will slip out from behind the terminal screws. If the line cord wires use circular eyelets (*Figure 4*) as connectors, the two terminal screws must be removed completely in order to disconnect the line cord wires. Take care not to drop the terminal screws into the iron if it becomes necessary to remove them. Refer to Section II, General Repair Procedures, Terminal and Wire Connectors, for further information.

8. Remove the line cord by prying the cord sleeve out of the recess in the handle. (*Figure 4*)

FIG.2

TERMINAL COVER
PLATE

TERMINAL
COVER
PLATE SCREW

FIG.3

TERMINAL
COVER PLATE
SCREW

TERMINAL COVER
PLATE(REMOVED)

HANDLE RECESS

PUSH-ON
CONNECTORS

FIG.4

CORD SLEEVE

EYELETS

9. Cut the line cord as close to the metal cord stop as possible with a pair of heavy poultry or sewing shears and remove the cord stop. (*Figure 5*)

10. Slide the cord sleeve off the line cord.

   NOTE: Both the cord stop and cord sleeve must be reinstalled on the new replacement line cord.

11. Slip the terminal ends of the new line cord through the cord sleeve.

12. Widen the metal cord stop with a pair of pliers. Place it on the line cord (about ¾ of an inch above the wire ends). Clamp the cord stop securely to the line cord by squeezing it with a pair of pliers. (*Figure 6*)

13. Slide cord sleeve firmly against the cord stop.

14. Place cord sleeve into recess in handle and connect wire ends to terminal posts. Position wires so that no strain is placed on terminal posts and make certain that terminal posts *do not* touch each other.

15. Replace the terminal cover plate.

   SPECIAL NOTE: To extend the life of a line cord, never wrap the line cord around the handle of an iron for storage. Coil it loosely beside the iron.

FIG.5

SHEARS

CORD SLEEVE

CORD
STOP

FIG.6

CORD SLEEVE

CORD
STOP

PLIERS

CORD STOP
WIDEN HERE

Problem Solver #5

APPLIANCE: Clothes Irons (Steam and Spray Type)

PROBLEM: **Iron does not spray water.**

EXPLANATION: There are two methods most commonly used by manufacturers to produce the water spray action in steam and spray irons. One type operates as a simple hand pump (similar to the hand pumps used to dispense hand lotion, perfume, and cleaners from bottles). The second type employs the pressure created by its own steam system to produce the water spray action. The hand pump can be identified in two ways:

A.   A single spray of water is produced when the spray button is depressed and ceases when the button reaches the bottom of its stroke.

B.   The small orifice in the spray nozzle that emits the water spray is uncovered and visible.

The pressure spray iron is identified by the continuous spray of water (and steam) emitted when the spray button is held down. It is further identified by a sliding cap that moves up and allows water to be sprayed from the spray nozzle orifice when the spray button is depressed. It moves down to cover and close the water spray orifice when the spray button is released.

The size of the water spray orifice in both spray systems is extremely small. Therefore, when either kind fails to produce a water spray, the orifice must be checked for and cleared of any foreign particles that may have clogged it.

TOOLS AND MATERIALS NEEDED:

(a) a single fine bristle (natural or nylon), at least ¾ of an inch long, removed from a clothes brush or hairbrush

(b) a pair of eyebrow tweezers

SOLUTION: 1.   Locate and identify the water spray orifice. (*Figures 1 and 2*)

FIG.1

SPRAY
ORIFICE

FIG.2

SPRAY
ORIFICE

2. To clear exposed orifice (*Figure 3*) hold brush bristle at one end with tweezers and insert other bristle end into orifice opening. Make certain that the thickness of the bristle is not larger than the orifice opening and that the bristle is stiff enough to exert pressure upon any foreign particle that may be stuck in the orifice. Bristle must pass through orifice opening.

3. To clear capped orifice (used in pressure systems), depress the spray button. This will raise the cap to expose the orifice. (*Figure 4*)

   NOTE: If cap does not rise to expose the orifice, the spray mechanism has a serious mechanical defect, and the iron should be taken to a qualified appliance repair shop.

4. Hold the spray button in the depressed position and insert the bristle end through the orifice.

5. Retest spray operation of iron. If spray operation has not been restored, iron should be taken to a qualified appliance service shop for further testing and repair.

FIG.3

BRISTLE

SPRAY BUTTON

FIG.4

SPRAY ORIFICE

Problem Solver #6

APPLIANCE: Clothes Irons (Steam and Regular)

PROBLEM: Iron does not shut off.

EXPLANATION: When an iron continues to heat after the fabric indicator knob has been placed in the "off" position, it
means either that the thermostat needs adjustment or
that the electrical contact points of the thermostat are
stuck in a closed position. Jammed thermostat contact
points present a more serious problem, and in addition
to not shutting off, the iron will heat to extremely high
temperatures, often causing aluminum sole plates to
melt. When this condition is suspected, discontinue
using the iron to avoid permanently damaging the sole
plate, and have iron serviced by a qualified appliance
technician. In most cases, however, adjusting the
thermostat (when no evidence of extreme overheating
exists) will allow the iron to shut off when the fabric
indicator knob is set to the "off" position.

TOOLS AND MATERIALS NEEDED:

(a) a small screwdriver (sewing machine type)

(b) a paper clip

(c) a pair of pliers

SOLUTION: 1. Remove line cord plug from wall outlet and allow
iron to cool to room temperature.

SPECIAL NOTE: *Figures 1 and 2* represent two of the
more common kinds of irons. Moreover, they are designed so that only a minimum number of parts need
be removed to gain access to the thermostat adjustment screw (or nut).

2. Set the fabric indicator knob to the "off" position.

FIG.1

STEAM CONTROL
BUTTON

FABRIC DIAL

SADDLE PLATE

FIG.2

CAP RIVET

STEAM CONTROL
KNOB

FABRIC DIAL
KNOB

3. To reach the thermostat adjustment screw for the iron illustrated in *Figure 1*, gently pry the metal saddle plate off by grasping and lifting both sides with fingertips. A stubborn saddle plate may be removed by carefully prying one side up with the flat blade of a screwdriver.

4. With saddle plate removed, locate the slotted thermostat adjustment screw. (*Figure 3*)

5. Insert screwdriver blade into the thermostat adjustment screw slot and give the adjustment screw a quarter turn in a clockwise direction.

6. Plug the line cord into the wall outlet. Make sure fabric indicator knob is still set to the "off" position. Check to see whether or not iron heats up.

7. If iron does not heat in "off" position, adjustment has corrected the condition and no further adjustment is necessary. Replace the saddle plate.

8. If iron continues to heat in "off" position, remove the line cord from the wall outlet. When the iron has cooled to room temperature, give the thermostat adjustment screw an additional quarter turn clockwise.

9. Retest iron in "off" position. Repeat the adjustment once more if necessary.

FIG.3

SCREW   ¼ TURN

ARROWS DENOTE
CLOCKWISE
DIRECTION

THERMOSTAT
ADJUSTMENT SCREW

SADDLE PLATE
SHOWN REMOVED

10. If adjustments do not prevent the iron from heating in the "off" position, the indication is that the thermostat is stuck and will probably have to be replaced. Further testing and repairs should be performed by a qualified appliance technician.

11. To reach the thermostat adjustment nut for the iron shown in *Figure 2,* bend a paper clip as shown in *Figure 4.* Place the tip of the paper clip in the center of the plastic cap rivet located on the iron handle, and press firmly down until the rivet is pushed clear through into the handle.

12. Grasp the front cap of the iron handle and pull it forward slowly. Disconnect the steam control lever from the top of the valve shaft and remove the front cap. (*Figure 5*)

CAUTION: Retrieve the cap rivet, which will be found in a little well directly below its position in the handle. Set it aside carefully so that it may be reinstalled after the thermostat adjustment is completed.

FIG.4

PAPER CLIP

CAP RIVET

STEAM CONTROL LEVER

FRONT CAP

CAP RIVET (REMOVED)

FIG.5

STEAM VALVE SHAFT

STEAM CONTROL LEVER

VALVE NUT

THERMOSTAT CONTROL CAM

13. Unscrew the valve nut (turn counter-clockwise) with pliers and remove the nut. Lift off the washer and the thermostat control cam. (*Figure 6A*)

14. Locate the thermostat adjustment nut. (*Figure 6*) Grasp the adjustment nut with fingers and give it a half turn in a clockwise direction. If nut is stubborn, grasp nut with pliers to turn it. (*Figure 6B*) Use moderate pressure only.

15. Replace the thermostat control cam, washer, and valve nut. Tighten valve nut securely with pliers. Connect the steam control lever to the top of the valve shaft and slide the front cap into place. Install the cam rivet. Press rivet firmly into place with the flat portion of the pliers.

16. Retest iron on "off" position. If iron does not heat, adjustment has corrected condition. Repeat the adjustment if necessary.

NOTE: If iron fails to respond to adjustments and continues to heat in the "off" position, have iron checked by qualified appliance technician.

FIG.6   EXPLODED VIEW

FIG.6A

PLIERS

VALVE NUT

WASHER

COUNTER CLOCKWISE

THERMOSTAT CONTROL CAM

STEAM VALVE SHAFT

THERMOSTAT ADJUSTMENT NUT

FIG.6B

THERMOSTAT ADJUSTMENT NUT

Problem Solver #7

APPLIANCE: Clothes Irons (Steam and Regular)

PROBLEM: **Iron burns cloth.**

EXPLANATION: When this happens, it is obvious that the iron temperature is too hot for the material being pressed. Excessive iron temperature may be caused by an incorrect setting of the fabric indicator knob or a malfunctioning thermostat.

TOOLS AND MATERIALS NEEDED:

(a) a dial thermometer
(used for candymaking and deep frying)

(b) a small screwdriver (sewing machine type)

(c) a paper clip

(d) a pair of pliers

(e) cooking oil

SOLUTION:

1. Make certain that the fabric indicator knob is correctly set for fabric to be pressed.

   NOTE: Modern fabrics contain a variety of synthetic fibers. Identifying these fibers and knowing the correct ironing temperature to use are important for their protection. Always follow the fabric or garment manufacturer's washing and ironing recommendations. When the composition of the fabric is unknown or whenever there is doubt concerning the correct ironing temperature to use, begin ironing with the fabric indicator control knob set to the lowest heat position.

2. If iron is correctly set for the fabric being ironed but the iron still burns the fabric, the iron must be checked to determine if the correct temperature is being maintained by the thermostat.

3. Set the fabric indicator knob to the lowest "synthetics" position on the fabric dial.

4. Plug the iron into wall outlet and allow iron to heat for at least three minutes.

   CAUTION: When testing steam irons, make certain water has been removed and iron is completely dry.

5. Dip the end of the liquid thermometer (about two inches) into clean cooking oil. Turn the iron upside down and place the thermometer on the sole plate. (*Figure 1*) Hold thermometer steady so that good contact is made with the sole plate. The cooking oil will help to transfer the heat of the sole plate to the thermometer for a more accurate thermometer reading.

6. The thermometer should slow to a stop at a temerature between 220° and 280° F. If the thermometer reads above this range, it indicates that the iron thermostat is not working properly and is allowing the iron to overheat.

FIG.1

CAUTION AND NOTE: If the thermometer pointer goes beyond the 400° F. mark when the iron is set for "synthetics," it means that the iron thermostat is jammed. Do not attempt any further checks. Disconnect the iron immediately from the wall outlet to prevent further damage to the sole plate of the iron. Jammed or otherwise defective thermostats should be replaced by qualified appliance repair technicians. If, however, the thermometer pointer indicates excessive iron temperature just above the normal range (220°-280° F.), an attempt can be made to adjust the thermostat to restore correct ironing temperatures. The procedures for adjusting the thermostat in two of the more widely used irons are given in the steps that follow.

7. Remove the iron plug from the wall outlet.

8. To reach the thermostat adjustment screw for the type of iron shown in *Figure 2*, gently pry the metal saddle plate off by grasping and lifting both sides with fingertips. A stubborn saddle plate may be removed by carefully prying one side up with the tip of a flatblade screwdriver.

    CAUTION: The saddle plate rests upon a plastic portion of the iron handle. If a screwdriver must be used, take care not to pry against the plastic handle.

9. Locate the slotted thermostat adjustment screw. (*Figure 2*) Insert the tip of a small screwdriver into the slot of the thermostat adjustment screw and give the screw a quarter turn in a clockwise direction.

10. Connect iron to wall outlet and measure the temperature of the sole plate again. Be sure to wait at least three minutes and check to see that the fabric indicator knob is on lowest "synthetics" setting. The temperature of the iron should now be lower.

FIG.2

SCREW

¼ TURN

ARROWS
DENOTE
CLOCKWISE
DIRECTION

THERMOSTAT
ADJUSTMENT
SCREW

SADDLE PLATE
(SHOWN REMOVED)

If, however, the temperature has not been lowered enough, turn the adjustment screw again (a quarter turn at a time) until temperature falls within correct range (220°-280° F.).

11. For the final test, turn the iron off and allow it to cool to room temperature. When the iron has cooled, place the fabric indicator knob in the lowest heat position. Plug the iron into wall receptacle. If iron does not heat, it means that the thermostat did not respond to the adjustment, is defective, and must be replaced.

12. To reach the thermostat adjustment nut for the type of iron shown in *Figure 3*, bend a paper clip as shown in *Figure 3* and place the tip of the paper clip in the center of the plastic cap rivet. Press down firmly until the rivet is pushed clear through the handle.

13. Grasp the front cap of the iron handle and pull it forward. Disconnect the steam control lever from the top of the valve shaft and remove the cap. (*Figure 4*)

    CAUTION: Retrieve the cap rivet, which will be found in a little well directly below its position in the handle. Set it aside carefully so that it may be reinstalled after the thermostat adjustment has been completed.

FIG.3

PAPER CLIP

STEAM CONTROL LEVER

CAP RIVET

FRONT CAP

FIG.4

STEAM VALVE SHAFT

STEAM
CONTROL
LEVER

VALVE
NUT

THERMOSTAT CONTROL CAM

14. Unscrew the valve nut (turn counter-clockwise) with pliers and remove it. Lift off the washer and the thermostat control cam. (*Figure 5*)

15. Locate the thermostat adjustment nut. (*Figure 5*) Grasp the adjustment nut with fingers and give it a half turn in a clockwise direction. If nut is stubborn, grasp it with pliers to turn it. Use only moderate pressure.

16. After adjustment has been made, replace the thermostat control cam washer and valve nut. Tighten valve nut securely with pliers and measure temperature of iron again. Repeat the adjustment (a half turn at a time) if necessary until temperature falls within the normal range (220°-280° F.).

17. Allow the iron to cool to room temperature for the final test. Set fabric indicator knob to the lowest heat position. Plug iron into wall outlet. If iron does not heat, it means that the thermostat did not respond to the adjustment, is defective, and therefore must be replaced. If iron does heat in the lowest position, the thermostat adjustment has been successfully completed.

18. Replace the steam control lever and slide the front clip cap into place.

19. Install the cam rivet. Press rivet into place firmly with the flat side of the pliers.

FIG.5   EXPLODED VIEW

VALVE NUT

THERMOSTAT CONTROL CAM

STEAM VALVE SHAFT

THERMOSTAT ADJUSTMENT
NUT

Problem Solver #8

APPLIANCE: All Toasters

PROBLEM: Toaster smokes.

EXPLANATION: The annoying and often frightening occurrence of smoke arising from a toaster is in almost all cases caused by crumbs or other food (butter, margarine, sugar, etc.) coming in contact with or accumulating close to the heating element wire. The problem is generally brought about by improper use and care of a toaster.

TOOLS AND MATERIALS NEEDED:

(a) a flashlight

(b) a ½" paintbrush

(c) clear household ammonia

SOLUTION:

1. Plug toaster into wall outlet and allow toaster to heat without bread.

   NOTE: Automatic self-lowering toasters can be operated without bread by momentarily pressing down on the bread carriage with the wooden (insulated) handle of the small paintbrush. (*Figure 1*)

2. As toaster heats, peer into bread slots and locate the exact area of heating element from which the smoke originates. (*Figure 2*)

3. Remove the line cord plug from the wall outlet and allow the toaster to cool to room temperature.

4. Carefully reexamine with flashlight the area where smoke originated to locate any particles of food stuck to heating element wire.

SMALL PAINT BRUSH

FIG.1

SELF LOWERING TYPE
AUTOMATIC TOASTER

BREAD CARRIAGE

LIGHT DARK

LIFT BREAD

BREAD
SLOT

FIG.2

HEATING
ELEMENT
UNIT

HEATING ELEMENT(NICHROME)
WIRE WOUND ON MICA OR
ASBESTOS SHEET

5. Insert paintbrush carefully through bread slot and gently brush the food particle off the heating element and down into the crumb tray. (*Figure 3*)

   CAUTION: Do not turn toaster upside down. Crumbs and other particles of food from the crumb tray will adhere to the heating element and cause a repetition of the smoking condition. More important, food particles coming in contact with the heating element wire produce "hot spots" (bright overheated spots on the heating element wire) that can cause the heating element to burn out.

6. Remove butter or margarine that may have gotten onto heating element or dripped into bottom of toaster by washing toaster areas with a paintbrush dipped into a solution of clear household ammonia. (*Figure 4*)

   CAUTION: Allow toaster to dry thoroughly (at least one hour) before attempting to use it.

   SPECIAL NOTE: To insure satisfactory service from your toaster:

   A. Brush the crumb tray clean regularly.

   B. Do not turn toaster upside down to remove crumbs.

   C. Avoid the practice of buttering bread *before* toasting it.

   D. Do not force oversized pieces of bread or other food items into toaster.

FIG.3

BREAD SLOTS

FIG.4

Problem Solver #9

APPLIANCE: All Toasters

PROBLEM: Toaster does not heat.

EXPLANATION: When the heating elements within a toaster do not heat, the cause can usually be traced to a blown fuse, a tripped circuit breaker, or a defective line cord.

TOOLS AND MATERIALS NEEDED:

(a) line cord (asbestos or plastic, as required by specific toaster; can be purchased completely assembled with plug and terminal connectors)

(b) a small screwdriver (sewing machine type)

(c) a pair of pliers

SOLUTION:

1. Make sure that the wall outlet has electric power. Plug a lamp or other appliance known to be in good working order into the outlet used for the toaster. If lamp or other appliance fails to operate, it can be assumed that a fuse has blown or that a circuit breaker has tripped "off," preventing electric power from reaching the wall outlet, or that the wall receptacle itself is defective. Refer to Section II, General Repair Procedures, Fuses and Circuit Breakers, for further information about this condition. However, if lamp or other appliance operates, it means that the problem is in the toaster.

2. Examine the line cord plug. Check the plug prongs for looseness. Test the condition of the line cord wires going into the plug by tugging firmly on the plug against the line cord. (*Figure 1*) If the plug prongs wiggle freely or if the plug seems to part from the line cord when pulled, the plug should be replaced. See Section II, General Repair Procedures, Plugs, for further information.

FIG.1

POINT WHERE WIRES
OFTEN BREAK

POINT WHERE WIRES
OFTEN BREAK

SPECIAL NOTE: While it is possible for wires to break anywhere along the length of the line cord, they are most apt to break at points where sharp bending occurs during use. These points are located where the line cord enters the plug and again where the line cord enters the toaster. When you are uncertain about breakage or whenever the line cord shows outward signs of wear, such as fraying, replace the entire line cord as outlined in the steps that follow.

CAUTION: Remove the line cord from the wall outlet before working on toaster.

3. Examine toaster shell and plastic base where line cord enters toaster. Locate and remove only those screws that fasten the section (usually part of the plastic base) through which the line cord enters the toaster. Separate this section from the toaster shell. (*Figure 2*)

4. Take careful note of the way the line cord wire ends are routed to insure correct routing of new replacement line cord wires.

5. Follow the line cord wire ends to where they end (toaster terminals) and note the kind of terminal connectors used. (*Figure 2*) If wires are attached with push-on connectors, simply grasp each connector with the fingertips and pull upward with a slight side to side motion and remove them. (*Figure 2A*)

6. If wires are attached with terminal screws, loosen the two screws with two counter-clockwise turns and remove the line cord wire ends.

NOTE AND CAUTION: If the line cord wire ends under the screws have U-shaped connectors, the wire ends will slip out from behind the terminal screws when the screws are loosened. (*Figure 2*) If the line cord wires use circular eyelets as connectors, the two terminal screws must be removed completely in order to disconnect the line cord wires.

Take care not to drop the terminal screws into the toaster if it becomes necessary to remove them. Refer to Section II, General Repair Procedures, Terminal and Wire Connectors, for further information.

FIG.2

FIG.2A

TERMINAL
SCREWS

FEED THROUGH TYPE
LINE CORD STOP

PLASTIC BASE
SECTION

7. Free the line cord by removing the line cord stop. If line cord is held by plastic feed-through type of cord stop, grip the cord stop with the tip of a pair of pliers. (*Figure 3*) Squeeze hard on plier handles and pull cord stop and cord wire out. Set cord stop aside for reuse with new replacement line cord.

8. Feed the wire ends of the new replacement line cord through the opening in the toaster section. Place the line cord stop at a distance from the line cord wire ends equal to its original position on the old line cord.

9. Clamp cord stop down firmly on line cord with pliers and push cord stop into place.

10. Connect the line cord wire ends to the toaster terminals (screw or push-on).

11. Route the wire ends of the line cord as they were originally.

12. Reattach toaster section and secure it with screws.

    CAUTION: When reassembling toaster, make certain that the line cord wires are not pinched between parts.

FIG.3

Problem Solver #10

APPLIANCE: All Toasters

PROBLEM: **One side of bread does not toast.**

EXPLANATION: A two-slice toaster may contain as many as four separate heating element units (one for each bread side).
When one or more of these element units fails to heat,
the side of the bread that faces the defective heating
element will not be toasted. The failure of one or more
heating element units to heat is usually traced to a
broken or burned-out heating element (nichrome) wire.

TOOLS AND MATERIALS NEEDED:

(a) a flashlight

(b) a lead pencil (sharpened)

(c) a pair of long-nose pliers

(d) terminal connector
(solderless spade for #16 wire, available at any
electrical hardware store)

SOLUTION: 1. Identify the defective heating element unit. (The
heating element facing the untoasted side of the
bread.)

2. Remove the line cord plug from the wall outlet
and allow the toaster to cool to room temperature.

3. Use flashlight to provide light inside the toaster.
Gently probe along the element wire to pinpoint
the exact location of the wire break. (*Figure 1*)

FIG.1

BREAK IN ELEMENT WIRE

HEATING ELEMENT UNIT

NOTE: Some breaks in the heating element wire are easily discovered by visual inspection, since a space may be seen between the parted wire ends. At times, however, the space between the parted element wires may be too small to be noticed and will therefore require gentle probing (with the point of a pencil) to disclose the break.

4. If a search through bread slots (at the top of toaster) fails to disclose the wire break, open or remove the bread crumb tray and continue to examine the element unit through the bottom of the toaster.

   NOTE: When a break in the heating element wire cannot be found or if, when located, the space between the two parted wire ends is more than one-half inch, the toaster should be taken to a qualified appliance service shop for further tests and repairs. If the parted wire ends are found to be close together, they may be mended as is described in the steps that follow.

5. Reach into toaster (through top bread slots or bottom with crumb tray opened) with a pair of long-nose pliers. Grasp and pull the wire ends toward each other so that they overlap or at least meet. (*Figure 2*)

   CAUTION: Use moderate force when adjusting wire ends in order to prevent further damage to them.

6. Bend a wire connector until the cylindrical sleeve breaks off from the front position of the connector. (*Figure 3*)

FIG.2

LONG NOSE PLIERS

BROKEN WIRE ENDS
BROUGHT TOGETHER

FIG.3

BREAK TERMINAL
CONNECTOR

LONG NOSE PLIERS

7. Grip the connector sleeve with the tip of the long-nose pliers and slip the sleeve over both ends of the heating element wire. (*Figure 4*)

8. Carefully adjust the sleeve so that it covers both ends of the wire equally. Crush the sleeve flat between the jaws of the pliers so that both wire ends are locked together securely. (*Figure 5*)

   NOTE: To obtain greater crushing power from the long-nose pliers, grip the sleeve as far back in the plier jaws (towards the hinge) as space permits.

9. Prod the sleeve with a pencil to see that wire ends are being held firmly. Crush the sleeve again if necessary.

10. Test the toaster operation. Plug the line cord into the wall outlet, allow toaster to heat (without bread), and check the repaired element. Element should glow red.

11. Inspect the mended sleeve connection. If it glows with the same degree of redness as does the wire of the heating element, the repair has been properly completed. If, however, slight sparking is noticed at the sleeve connection or if the sleeve connection glows brighter (more white hot than red) than the rest of the element wire, it means that the sleeve connection has not been properly made (loose). The sleeve connector should therefore be removed and the connection remade with a new connector sleeve.

    SPECIAL NOTE: With normal use, the heating element units of toasters will operate for many years without failure. In most instances a defective heating element can be traced to improper use of a toaster. To avoid damaging the heating element units of your toaster, follow the suggestions listed below.

    A. Make sure that food items to be toasted do not come in contact with the heating element wires.

    B. Do not remove particles of food that have stuck to the heating element units with hard, sharp objects. Remove food particles with a brush after the toaster has cooled.

FIG.4

LONG NOSE PLIERS

CONNECTOR SLEEVE

FIG.5

CONNECTOR SLEEVE PLACED OVER WIRE ENDS

CONNECTOR SLEEVE CRUSHED TO SECURE WIRE ENDS

C. Do not attempt to dislodge food items that have become stuck in the bread slots with a fork; a fork may curve into and break the heating element wires.

CAUTION: Disconnect the line cord from the wall outlet before attempting to remove any food that may have become lodged in the bread slots. If food being toasted cannot be removed by lifting the bread carriage lever, carefully insert the tip of a small steak knife into the food item and pry the item straight up. Make certain that the knife blade is kept parallel with the bread slot. Never allow it to touch the heating element units.

Problem Solver #11

APPLIANCE: Automatic Pop-Up Toasters

PROBLEM: Bread does not stay down.

EXPLANATION: Bread is lowered and raised in a toaster by the bread carriage and rack. In its lowered position, the bread carriage engages and is locked by a latch down mechanism. Through normal use, the latching mechanism may bend out of adjustment or bind at hinged points and thus fail to lock the bread carriage in its lowered position. While many variations of latching mechanisms are used in different toaster models, most are simple in design, and their operation is easily understood.

TOOLS AND MATERIALS NEEDED:

> (a) a pair of universal pliers
>
> (b) a pair of long-nose pliers
>
> (c) a small artist's paintbrush
>
> (d) non-inflammable cleaning fluid
> (capable of dissolving grease)

SOLUTION:

> NOTE: The latch down mechanism is located on the side of the toaster that contains the bread lever and toast control knobs. Access to the latch down mechanism may be achieved by disassembling the plastic base section and/or a section of the metal toaster shell. *Figures 1, 3, and 6* illustrate common varieties of construction. Other toaster models require the removal of the entire toaster shell to gain access to the latch down mechanism and should, therefore, be taken to a qualified appliance repair shop for service.

> 1. Identify the toaster's construction according to *Figures 1, 3, and 6.*

> 2. To disassemble toaster shown in *Figure 1,* remove the bread lever knob by pulling it straight out. Take care not to lose the small metal clasp that secures the knob to the lever. (*Figure 1*)

> NOTE: As an aid to removing a stubborn knob, wedge the flat tip of a screwdriver behind the knob and pry it off.

> 3. Remove the small toast control lever and knob set screw located on the bottom of the toaster, and pull the toast control lever and knob out. (*Figure 1*)

4. Remove the two screws that fasten the plastic base to the metal shell and remove the plastic base. (*Figure 2*)

5. Grasp the bottom edge of the front metal shell section and pull down hard until the locking tabs are freed from the locking tab slots. Lift the front metal shell section away from the toaster. (*Figure 2*)

6. Examine the operation of the latch down mechanism after the plastic base or end shell section has been removed. Operate the bread lever and note the condition that prevents the "latch" from engaging or locking onto the "latch lock." (*Figure 2A*)

7. If the latch fails to engage the latch lock (they do not make contact), examine the latch, bread lever, and bread rack for bent parts. Realign any bent part by bending it back into position with a pair of pliers.

8. If the latch engages (touches) the latch lock but does not lock, examine the electromagnetic latch release and the latch lock to see if they move freely on their pivots. (*Figure 2A*)

9. Free a stuck pivot or hinge by cleaning it thoroughly with a non-inflammable cleaning fluid applied with a small artist's brush. Work the movable latch lock and electromagnetic latch release back and forth to allow the cleaning fluid to penetrate until free movement is obtained.

    CAUTION: Do not lubricate a pivot or hinge on the latch down mechanism.

10. If the latch lock and electromagnetic latch release move freely but the latch still fails to hold, look to see that the flat, leaf-shaped spring between the solenoid coil and the electromagnetic latch release has sufficient tension to position the electromagnetic latch release to its locking position (away from the solenoid so as to engage the latch lock).

FIG.1

PLASTIC BASE

TOAST CONTROL LEVER AND KNOB

BREAD LEVER KNOB

SET SCREW

METAL SHELL SECTION (REMOVED)

FIG.2

LOCKING TAB SLOTS

PLASTIC BASE

LOCKING TABS

LATCHING MECHANISM ENLARGED VIEW

FIG.2A

ELECTRO-MAGNETIC LATCH RELEASE

HINGE

SOLENOID

LEAF SPRING

LATCH

PIVOT

LATCH LOCK

LATCH SHOWN IN LOCKED POSITION

11. If the leaf spring (*Figure 2A*) does not push the electromagnetic latch release out far enough to engage the latch lock, bend the leaf spring out slightly with long-nose pliers.

12. Reassemble toaster and test latch down action. To reassemble toaster, simply reverse the procedure outlined in steps 2, 3, 4, and 5.

    NOTE: Make certain that the locking tabs of the metal shell section are completely seated in the locking tab slots to insure satisfactory alignment of all parts.

13. To disassemble toaster shown in *Figure 3*, remove the bread lever knob and the toast control knob by pulling them straight out. (*Figure 3*)

14. Remove the plastic shell section mounting screw with a pair of pliers. (*Figure 4*)

15. Grasp the plastic shell section and pull it downward until the spring clasp that fastens it at the top to the metal shell is released to free the shell section. (*Figure 4*)

16. Examine the operation of the latch down mechanism. (*Figure 5*) Operate the bread lever and note the condition that prevents the latch from engaging or locking onto the latch lock. (*Figure 5A*)

17. If the latch does not engage (touch) the latch lock, check the position of the latch lock with respect to the latch. The latch lock should be struck by the latch when the bread carriage is lowered. Bend the latch lock toward the latch (if necessary) until correct striking action is achieved.

18. If the latch engages the latch lock but does not lock, check to see that the latch goes below the latch lock lip when the bread carriage is lowered. (*Figure 5A*) If it does not, check along the bread carriage and bread carriage guide rod for any obstruction that could prevent the bread carriage from being lowered fully.

FIG.3

METAL SHELL

BREAD
LEVER
KNOB

TOAST CONTROL
KNOB

LIGHT 1·3·5·7·9 DARK

FIG.4

PLASTIC SHELL
SECTION

LIGHT 1·3·5·7·9 DARK

MOUNTING SCREW

FIG.5

BREAD CARRIAGE
GUIDE ROD

SOLENOID

FIG.5A

LATCH

LATCH
LOCK

ELECTRO-MAGNETIC
LATCH LOCK RELEASE

SOLENOID

19. Reassemble the toaster and test the latch down operation. For reassembling instructions follow steps 13, 14, and 15 in reverse order.

NOTE: When reassembling the toaster, make sure that the metal clasp at the top of the plastic shell section engages the edge of the metal toaster shell.

20. To gain access to the latch down mechanism for the toaster illustrated in *Figure 6*, remove the toast control knob by pulling it straight out.

21. Remove the two screws that fasten the front plate. Depress the door release bar to raise the door and door handle. Lift the front plate (escutcheon) out. (*Figure 6*)

FIG.6

ONE SLICE

OVEN   TOASTER   TOP BROWN ONLY

FRONT PLATE (REMOVED)

TOAST CONTROL KNOB
(PULL STRAIGHT OUT)

FRONT PLATE FASTENING SCREWS

22. Examine the operation of the latching mechanism by closing the door. (*Figures 7 and 7A*) Check to see that the door latch is aligned with the door latch pin. If necessary, bend the door latch or door latch pin with a pair of pliers until the door latch strikes the door latch pin correctly.

23. If the door latch engages the door latch pin correctly but the door does not lock, check to see that the latch spring is properly seated and that it has enough tension to operate the latch and latch lock.

24. Check for free movement of both the latch and latch lock. If either does not move freely upon its pivot, clean the pivot. (*Figure 7A*) Refer to step 9 for cleaning procedures.

25. Reassemble toaster and test the latch down operation.

FIG.7

LATCHING MECHANISM
ENLARGED VIEW

FIG.7A

DOOR LATCH

DOOR LATCH PIN

PIVOT

LATCH

LATCH LOCK

ELECTROMAGNETIC
LATCH
RELEASE

LATCH SPRING

PIVOT

Problem Solver #12

APPLIANCE: Automatic Pop-Up Toasters

PROBLEM: Toaster does not pop up.

EXPLANATION: This condition occurs in automatic toasters when something goes wrong in either the latching or timer mechanisms. The latching mechanism is responsible for locking the bread carriage down during toasting, and the timer mechanism automatically limits the "down" time by tripping (unlocking) the latch to release the bread carriage after a prescribed period of toasting time has elapsed. The types of defects that can be encountered in these mechanisms are numerous. Some are serious and require the services of a qualified appliance technician. Others are relatively minor and may require only a simple adjustment or repair. The steps outlined under "solution" below cover common defects that are easily corrected.

TOOLS AND MATERIALS NEEDED:

(a) a pair of long-nose pliers

(b) a ¾" paintbrush

(c) an artist's paintbrush

(d) a #0 knitting needle

(e) a flashlight

(f) cleaning fluid
(non-inflammable grease solvent type)

SOLUTION: 1. Remove the line cord from the wall outlet. Depress the bread lever and latch the bread carriage down in its toasting position. Lift the bread lever (bread release knob on some toaster models) to pop up the bread carriage. If the bread carriage is difficult to raise manually, it indicates either that the carriage is jamming in the carriage support slots (*Figure 1*) or that the latching mechanism is not releasing the carriage properly. If the bread carriage can be lowered and raised manually but fails to pop up automatically, the problem is in the toaster timer.

FIG.1

BREAD CARRIAGE

CARRIAGE SUPPORT
SLOTS

2. When the bread carriage fails to release properly with manual operation, check along the carriage support slots and make certain that the bread carriage is not binding. The bread carriage may bind when burned particles of food have become lodged in the carriage support slots or when the bread carriage is bent out of alignment.

   NOTE: Light the inside of the toaster with a flashlight.

3. Clear burned food from carriage support slots with knitting needle and brush clean with paintbrush. (*Figure 2*)

4. Straighten bread carriage (if necessary) so that it moves up and down freely in the carriage support slots by bending slightly with the long-nose pliers. (*Figure 3*)

5. If the bread carriage moves freely when operated manually but fails to pop up automatically during use, inspect both the latching mechanism and timer.

   CAUTION: Some toasters have the words "one slice" stamped on the top of the shell. When used to toast only a single slice of bread, these toasters require that the bread slice be placed in the slot indicated by arrows for correct timer operation. Failure to do so will cause bread placed in the other slot to burn long before popping up.

   NOTE: Refer to Problem Solver #11 for the procedure for gaining access to and servicing the latch down mechanism of three common types of toasters.

6. After testing and servicing the latch down mechanism, retest the toaster for automatic pop-up during actual use. If bread carriage still does not pop up during use, the problem lies in the toaster timer. The toaster should then be taken to a qualified appliance service shop for further tests and repairs.

FIG.2

CARRIAGE SUPPORT SLOTS

KNITTING
NEEDLE

FIG.3

PLIERS

BREAD CARRIAGE

Problem Solver #13

APPLIANCE: Automatic Pop-Up Toasters

PROBLEM: **Bread toasts too light or too dark.**

EXPLANATION: This complaint can often be traced to the type of bread used. Since different breads may contain different quantities of moisture and ingredients such as milk, butter, sugar, and so forth, each may require a different toasting time to achieve the same degree of toast color. If, however, the resulting toast color varies on the usual control setting when the same bread is used, the toaster timer probably needs adjustment.

TOOLS AND MATERIALS NEEDED:

   (a) a small screwdriver (sewing machine type)

   (b) a pair of pliers

SOLUTION: 1. Check to see that the toast control knob has not been accidentally moved from the desired setting.

   SPECIAL NOTE: The toast control knob adjusts the timer mechanism to lengthen or shorten the toasting period, for darker or lighter toast. In addition to this control knob, each toaster is provided with a second timer adjustment that is used to calibrate the toast control knob so that it indicates the degree of toast color accurately. Some toaster models make this timer adjustment readily available for the user by providing a timer adjustment knob on the underside of the toaster. (*Figure 1*) Most models, however, locate a timer adjustment screw or cam inside the metal toaster shell. (*Figures 3 and 4*)

   CAUTION: Some toasters have the words "one slice" stamped on the top of the shell. When only a single slice of bread is to be toasted, these toasters require that the bread slice be placed in the slot indicated by arrows for correct timer operation. Failure to do so will cause bread placed in the other slot to toast too dark or burn long before it pops up.

   2. To adjust the toaster timer (*Figure 1*), set the bread control knob to its middle position ("medium" toast). Toast two slices of bread and observe the degree of toasting.

FIG.1

UNDERSIDE VIEW

TIMER ADJUSTMENT
KNOB (THERMOSTAT)

3. If toast color is lighter than medium, remove plug from outlet, allow toaster to cool, and turn the timer adjustment knob one click toward "dark." Retest by toasting bread. Turn adjustment knob further if necessary, until desired medium toast is obtained.

4. If toast color is darker than medium, turn the timer adjustment knob one turn toward "light." Turn adjustment knob further toward "light" if necessary, until desired medium toast is obtained.

   NOTE: The toasters illustrated in *Figures 2 and 4* are examples of common types that require removal of a section of their shells in order to reach the timer adjustments.

5. Identify your toaster's construction according to *Figures 2 and 4.*

6. To gain access to the timer for the toaster shown in *Figure 2*, remove the bread lever knob and the toast control knob by pulling them straight out. (*Figure 2*)

7. Remove the plastic shell section mounting screw with a pair of pliers. (*Figure 3*)

8. Grasp the plastic shell section and pull it downward until the spring clasp that fastens it at the top to the metal shell is released to free the shell section. (*Figure 3*)

9. Locate the timer adjustment screw. (*Figure 3A*) If medium toast is too light, turn the adjustment screw (a half turn at a time) in a clockwise direction with a small screwdriver. If medium toast is too dark, turn the adjustment screw (a half turn at a time) in a counter-clockwise direction. Test toast color between each half turn of adjustment by toasting bread with the bread control set in its middle position ("medium" toast).

FIG. 2

METAL SHELL SECTION

LIGHT 1 • 3 • 5 • 7 • 9 DARK

BREAD CONTROL KNOB
(PULL STRAIGHT OUT)

BREAD
LEVER
KNOB

FIG. 3

PLASTIC SHELL
SECTION

LIGHT 1 • 3 • 5 • 7 • 9 DARK

FIG. 3A

MOUNTING SCREW
(REMOVE WITH PLIERS)

TIMER ADJUSTMENT
SCREW

NOTE: When reassembling the toaster, make sure that the metal clasp at the top of the plastic shell section fully engages the edge of the metal toaster shell.

10. To gain access to the timer for the toaster illustrated in *Figure 4*, remove the toast control knob by pulling it straight out.

11. Remove the two screws that fasten the front plate. Depress the door release bar to raise the door and door handle and lift the front plate (escutcheon) out. (*Figure 4*)

12. Locate the timer adjustment cam for toaster. (*Figure 4A*) If toast is too light for medium setting, insert the tip of a screwdriver into the cam slot (*Figure 4A*) and turn the cam (a quarter turn at a time) in a counter-clockwise direction. If toast is too dark for medium setting, turn adjustment cam (a quarter turn at a time) in a clockwise direction. Retest toast color after each quarter turn until desired medium toast is obtained.

CAUTION: Make certain bread slice is placed on side of toaster marked "one slice."

Problem Solver #14

APPLIANCE: All Toasters

PROBLEM: User gets an electric shock when metal shell of toaster is touched.

EXPLANATION: This condition occurs when one of the toaster components or wires that carry the electric current makes contact with any of the internal metal parts. The condition presents a serious hazard to the user of the toaster. Further use of the toaster should be discontinued until the condition has been corrected.

FIG. 4

START   OPEN

GENERAL ELECTRIC
TOASTER-OVEN.

(ONE SLICE)
OVEN   TOASTER   TOP
BROWN
ONLY

TOAST CONTROL KNOB
(PULL STRAIGHT OUT)

FRONT
PLATE
(REMOVED)

FRONT PLATE
FASTENING SCREW

FIG. 4A

TIMER ADJUSTING CAM

ENLARGED VIEW

TOOLS AND MATERIALS NEEDED:

(a) a pair of long-nose pliers

(b) a table lamp

(c) a 6-foot extension cord

(d) a flashlight

(e) a #0 knitting needle

(f) a sharp paring knife

SOLUTION:

1. Remove the line cord from the wall outlet. If toaster is hot, allow it to cool to room temperature.

2. Latch the bread carriage down in its toasting position.

3. Light the inside of the bread slots with a flashlight and carefully examine the heating element (nichrome) wires. Check to see that the wires do not at any point contact metal parts of the toaster such as the bread carriage or the bread guard wires. (*Figure 1*) Inspection should be made through the top bread slots and bottom opening with bread crumb tray opened or removed.

   NOTE: While it is possible for unwanted contact to be made between current-carrying parts and other metal components almost anywhere within the toaster, contact occurs most often when a portion of heating element wire extends too far into the bread slot or when the bread guard wires have been bent into the heating element wire.

4. Carefully adjust heating element wires or bread guard wires with the tip of a knitting needle or a pair of long-nose pliers so that there is sufficient space between the heating element wires and other metal parts of the toaster. (*Figure 2*)

5. Test toaster to make sure that the condition has been corrected.

FIG.1

BREAD SLOT

BREAD GUARD WIRES

HEATING ELEMENT UNIT

HEATING ELEMENT(NICHROME) WIRE WOUND ON MICA OR ASBESTOS SHEET

FIG.2

BOTTOM VIEW

LIGHT DARK

LONG NOSE PLIERS

HEATING ELEMENT WIRE

BREAD GUARD WIRE

SPECIAL NOTE: A simple testing circuit can be arranged with any available table lamp and a 6-foot extension cord. This testing circuit will provide an effective visual indication of whether or not the condition still exists. The procedure for arranging and using the test circuit is outlined in the steps that follow.

6. Separate the wires of the extension cord for about ten inches along the center of its length by slitting them apart with a sharp paring knife. (*Figure 3*) Guide the paring knife carefully along the center insulation of the extension cord to avoid exposing the copper wire.

7. Cut through one side of the separate extension cord wires with the paring knife. (*Figure 4*)

8. Remove about an inch of insulation from the cut wire ends. (*Figure 5*)

FIG.3

EXTENSION CORD
SOCKET

EXTENSION CORD

FIG.4

FIG.5

TEST LEAD ENDS

9. Wrap one cut wire end of the extension cord around one prong of the toaster plug. Connect the other wire end to any point on the metal shell of the toaster. Make certain wire end to toaster shell makes good contact with clean, unpainted surface. (*Figure 6*)

10. Connect lamp plug with extension cord receptacle. Connect extension cord plug with a convenient wall outlet. (*Figure 6*)

11. Turn on lamp switch. Depress bread lever down to toast position.

12. If lamp does not light, the hazardous condition has been corrected. The toaster is now safe for use.

13. If lamp lights, the condition still exists. Disconnect extension cord from wall outlet and reexamine toaster for unwanted connection between heating element wires and other metal parts. Retest toaster with test lamp circuit as before.

14. If unwanted connection cannot be located and test lamp circuit continues to indicate that the hazardous condition exists, toaster should not be used until properly repaired by a qualified appliance technician.

SPECIAL NOTE: The extension cord that has had a wire cut for the purpose of arranging the test lamp circuit may be restored for use as an extension cord by splicing the cut wire ends together. See Section II, General Repair Procedures, How to Install Solderless Wire Connectors.

FIG.6

TABLE LAMP

EXTENSION CORD

TOASTER

EXTENSION CORD
WIRE CONNECTS
TO ONE SIDE OF
PLUG

TOASTER LINE CORD

Problem Solver #15

APPLIANCE: Non-Automatic Broilers

PROBLEM: Heating element does not come on.

EXPLANATION: Many simply constructed broilers have no automatic features. Most do not have an "on-off" switch, so that they heat up when the line cord is plugged into a wall outlet, and they shut off when the line cord is disconnected. When this type of broiler fails to heat up, a search will usually disclose a broken wire or wire connection.

TOOLS AND MATERIALS NEEDED:

(a) a small screwdriver (sewing machine type)

(b) a pair of long-nose pliers

(c) a pair of universal pliers

(d) one sheet of fine sandpaper (#00)

SOLUTION: 1. Make sure that the wall outlet has electric power. Plug a lamp or other appliance known to be in good working order into the outlet used for the broiler. If lamp or other appliance fails to operate, it can be assumed that a fuse has blown, a circuit breaker has tripped off, thus preventing electric power from reaching the wall outlet, or that the outlet itself is defective. Refer to Section II, General Repair Procedures, Fuses, Circuit Breakers, and Wall Outlets, for further information about this condition. If the lamp or other appliance operates, it means that the problem is in the broiler.

2. Examine the broiler line cord. (*Figure 1*) Check the female appliance plug for heat damage. If portions of the plastic body are burned away and the terminal connectors are loose and corroded, replace the female appliance plug. Refer to Section II, General Repair Procedures, Plugs, for detailed information.

FIG.1

BROILER

TERMINAL POSTS

FEMALE APPLIANCE PLUG

TERMINAL
CONNECTORS

LINE CORD

MALE PLUG

PLUG PRONGS

NOTE: When in addition to a damaged female plug, examination of the line cord discloses a loose male plug and/or frayed wire covering, replace the entire line cord. The line cord may be purchased completely assembled from an appliance repair shop.

3. Inspect the terminal posts of the broiler. (*Figure 1*) If they are dark purple or black in color and are pitted (metal eaten away), clean them by rubbing with small strips of sandpaper until their surface becomes smooth and bright.

    CAUTION: Do not remove too much of the surface metal with sandpaper. Reducing the thickness of the terminal posts may result in a loose fit with the female appliance plug. This will cause further deterioration of both the plug and terminal posts. Terminal posts that have worn excessively thin must be replaced by a qualified appliance technician.

4. Check terminal posts for looseness by wiggling them from side to side. Tighten loose terminal posts. Reach into broiler with pliers and turn the back nut (clockwise) until terminal post is secure. (*Figure 2*)

    NOTE: The back nut may have become stuck to the thread of the terminal post. Therefore, when you turn the back nut, it may be necessary to hold the terminal post with another pair of pliers to prevent it from turning together with the back nut.

5. After the back nut has been tightened, tighten the front terminal nut to insure a good connection with the heating element wire.

6. Check the heating element wires going to the terminal posts. If wires are broken, reconnect them as outlined in Section II, General Repair Procedures, Heating Element Wire.

FIG.2

HEATING ELEMENT

HEATING ELEMENT WIRE

TERMINAL NUT

BACK NUT

MICA WASHERS

SIDE VIEW

WASHERS

FRONT TERMINAL NUT

CABINET

TERMINAL POST

HEATER ELEMENT WIRE

BACKNUT

MICA WASHERS

Problem Solver #16

APPLIANCE: Broilers

PROBLEM: Fuse blows or circuit breaker trips when broiler is turned on.

EXPLANATION: Fuses and circuit breakers are safety devices that automatically limit the amount of electric power a line may carry. A blown fuse or tripped circuit breaker (depending on which is employed) is an indication that the demand for electric power on that particular electric line exceeded the safety limit. This can happen when too many appliances are operated on the same electric line or when an appliance (in this case a broiler) becomes defective and creates a "short circuit."

TOOLS AND MATERIALS NEEDED:

(a) a pair of long-nose pliers

(b) a screwdriver

(c) fiberglass tape (heat-proof)

SOLUTION:
1. Disconnect the broiler from the wall outlet.

2. Do not remove the blown fuse or, if circuit breaker is used, do not reset it to the "on" position.

   NOTE: See Section II, General Repair Procedures, Fuses and Circuit Breakers, for further information.

3. Check to see if other appliances have gone "dead" as a result of the blown fuse. If other appliances are found not to be operating, the blown fuse or tripped circuit breaker may have resulted from the user's operating too many appliances on the same electric line.

   SPECIAL NOTE: The electric power consumption of broilers (and many other heat-producing appliances) is very near the maximum safe power delivery of an electric line. Local electrical wiring regulations usually require that a separate electric line leading to a single wall outlet be provided for use by an electrical appliance. When blown fuses are experienced regularly, consult your electrician about adequate wiring.

4. If investigation of other appliances eliminates the possibility of too many appliances on one line as the cause of the blown fuse or tripped circuit breaker, it can be assumed that a defect in the broiler has produced a short circuit.

NOTE AND CAUTION: A short circuit is produced when an unwanted electrical connection is made within the broiler. When a short circuit is suspected, do not attempt to use the broiler until the unwanted connection is located and removed. A careful inspection of the broiler wiring will often reveal the location of the unwanted connection. This procedure is outlined in the steps that follow.

5. Remove the side shell mounting screws with a pair of pliers or a screwdriver and set them carefully aside. (*Figure 1*)

FIG.1 TUBULAR TYPE HEATING ELEMENT

HEATING ELEMENT TERMINALS

SIDE SHELL

SIDE SHELL MOUNTING SCREWS

6. Pry the bottom of the side shell away from the broiler with the flat blade of a screwdriver. Lift and remove the side shell.

7. Examine the heating element terminals and the wires that connect to them. (*Figures 2 and 3*) Check to see that there is no connection being made between the two terminals. Check also to see that the terminal connectors are not touching the black metal sheath of the heating element. (*Figure 3*) Adjust wires and/or terminal connectors with long-nose pliers to provide clearance when necessary.

   CAUTION: The terminal connectors of the heating element can withstand only slight bending. (*Figure 2*) If it is necessary to adjust the terminal connectors, use extreme care to avoid breakage.

8. Inspect the wires leading to the heating element terminals and the "on-off" switch for frayed insulation covering. Cover frayed sections of wires with fiberglass tape. Refer to Section II, General Repair Procedures, Terminals and Wire Connectors, for more details on how to insulate wire.

FIG.2

ON-OFF SWITCH

FEMALE TERMINAL
CONNECTORS

BLACK METAL SHEATH

MALE TERMINAL
CONNECTORS

9. Check to see that wires were not pinched between sharp portions of the side shell and the broiler shell. This condition is sometimes evidenced by blackened burn marks at one or more points along the wire. Cover these points with fiberglass tape.

   NOTE: If cause of short circuit cannot be established, the broiler should be taken to a qualified appliance repair shop for further tests.

10. Replace the side shell and secure it with the mounting screws. Take care not to pinch the wires between the side shell and the broiler shell. Make certain that the heating element terminals do not contact the side shell.

11. Replace the blown fuse with a new one or reset the circuit breaker to "on" and operate the broiler.

FIG.3

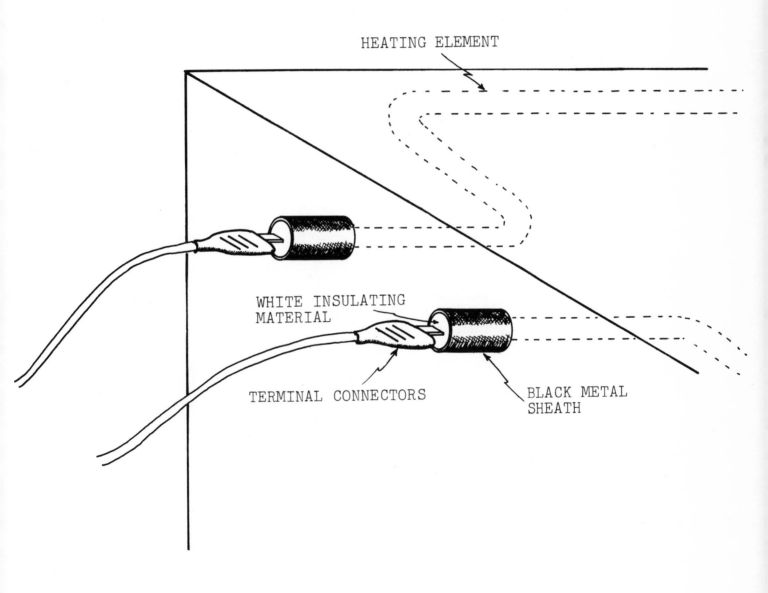

HEATING ELEMENT

WHITE INSULATING
MATERIAL

TERMINAL CONNECTORS

BLACK METAL
SHEATH

Problem Solver #17

APPLIANCE: Broilers

PROBLEM: Fuse blows or circuit breaker trips when broiler is plugged into wall outlet with switch in the "off" position.

EXPLANATION: When the fuse blows or circuit breaker trips to "off" with the broiler switch in the "off" position, it invariably points to a defective line cord. A close examination of the broiler line cord will probably disclose that the two wires that are normally insulated from each other have at some point contacted each other and caused a short circuit.

TOOLS AND MATERIALS NEEDED:

(a) a pair of pliers

(b) one heavy-duty male plug

(c) a 6-foot length of asbestos- and cloth-covered line cord wire

(d) a screwdriver

(e) fiberglass tape

SOLUTION: 1. Examine the line cord plug. If the plug shows signs of charring or if the wires going into it appear to have melted or fused together, the plug must be replaced. If no visible signs of defect are evident, pull the plug. If the plug parts from the line cord, replace the plug. See Section II, General Repair Procedures, Plugs, for information on how to replace the plug.

NOTE: Defective wires in line cords can often be hidden beneath the outer cloth covering. Therefore, to insure the elimination of a short circuit due to the line cord, replace the entire line cord. The procedure for this is outlined in the steps that follow.

2. Remove the two screws that fasten the side shell and set them carefully aside. (*Figure 1*)

FIG.1

SIDE SHELL

OFF
ON

SIDE SHELL MOUNTING
SCREWS

SCREWDRIVER

FIG.2

ON-OFF SWITCH

WIRE
NUTS

FEMALE TERMINAL
CONNECTORS

BLACK METAL SHEATH

MALE TERMINAL
CONNECTORS

3. Pry the bottom edge of the side shell with the flat tip of a screwdriver. Lift and remove the side shell. (*Figures 1 and 2*)

4. Remove the wire nuts by unscrewing them in a counter-clockwise direction. (*Figure 3*)

5. Twist apart the line cord wire ends from the wires to which they are connected. (*Figure 3*)

6. Free the line cord from the side shell by removing the line cord stop. The feed-through type cord stop is removed by gripping it with the tip of a pair of pliers. (*Figure 4*) Squeeze hard on the handles of the pliers, and pull the cord stop and line cord wire out. Set the cord stop carefully aside for reuse with new replacement line cord.

7. Feed the wire ends of the new replacement line cord through the opening in the side shell. Place the line cord stop at a distance from the line cord wire ends equal to its original position on the old line cord.

8. Clamp the cord stop firmly on the line cord with pliers and push the cord stop into place in the side shell.

FIG.3

CORD STOP

LINE CORD

BROILER SHELL

WIRE NUT

WIRE NUT

FIG.4   REMOVAL OF LINE CORD STOP WITH PLIERS

CORD STOP

LINE CORD STOP(ENLARGED)

9. Remove about an inch of insulation from each line cord wire end.

   CAUTION: Do not remove any more of the asbestos (white fluffy material) from the wire ends than is necessary.

10. Wrap the individual line cord wires with fiberglass tape. (*Figure 5*)

11. Reconnect the line cord wire ends to other wire ends as they were in the original line cord and replace the wire nuts. Refer to Section II, General Repair Procedures, Terminals and Wire Connectors, for more detailed information.

12. Reattach the side shell and secure it with screws.

    CAUTION: When reassembling, make sure wires are not pinched between sharp edges of side shell and broiler shell.

FIG.5

LINE CORD ENDS WRAPPED
WITH FIBERGLASS TAPE

Problem Solver #18

APPLIANCE: Coffee Makers (Electric)

PROBLEM: Coffee has poor flavor.

EXPLANATION: Coffee flavor may vary with different brands, and some are preferred because of their distinctive flavor. Some coffee, however, tastes bitter because the coffee maker has not been properly maintained. Good coffee maker maintenance should include cleaning that removes coffee residue and mineral deposits contained in hard water. These contaminants often accumulate in inaccessible areas within the coffee maker and are not readily removed by normal cleaning methods.

TOOLS AND MATERIALS NEEDED:

(a) one cup of white vinegar

(b) baking soda

(c) dishwashing detergent

(d) ordinary cooking pot

SOLUTION:
1. See *Figure 1* for illustration showing typical coffee maker and its component parts.

2. Rinse coffee maker, coffee basket, and pump tube thoroughly with clear water in order to remove coffee grounds.

FIG.1

SPREADER

LID

COFFEE
BASKET

POT

PUMP TUBE

COFFEE
STRENGTH
CONTROL KNOB

BASE

INDICATOR LAMP

3. Place coffee basket and pump tube in cooking pot. Add dishwashing detergent and fill pot to brim with hot water. Allow to soak for at least 15 minutes. (*Figure 2*)

   NOTE: Some coffee makers are designed with sealed bases and are featured as "completely immersible" models. Water is prevented from entering the working parts of these units for as long as the seals remain intact. Since the possibility of water leaking into the sealed base is ever present and since there is no greater cleaning advantage gained by immersing the entire coffee maker, it is advisable to follow the soaking method described as additional insurance to prolong satisfactory service.

4. Using dishwasher detergent and water, scrub coffee maker, coffee basket, and pump tube thoroughly with dishcloth. (*Figure 3*)

   CAUTION: Avoid use of abrasive cleaners and pads, which produce minute scratches in metal surfaces.

5. Rinse all parts well with warm water. Allow to dry completely before storing.

   SPECIAL NOTE: The foregoing cleaning and care procedures have been suggested for "after each use" care. The cleaning procedures to be described in the steps that follow are suggested as periodic treatments to remove any accumulation of deposits.

6. To remove mineral deposits, fill coffee maker with a solution of equal parts of white vinegar and water. Place coffee basket and pump tube in coffee maker and allow vinegar solution to boil through as when making coffee.

7. To remove coffee residue, dissolve approximately two teaspoons of baking soda (for 8-cup coffee makers) in water. Allow solution to boil through as when making coffee.

FIG.2

DETERGENT SOLUTION

COFFEE BASKET

PUMP TUBE

COOKING POT

FIG.3

COFFEE BASKET

COOKING POT

PUMP TUBE

DISH CLOTH

Problem Solver #19

APPLIANCE: Coffee Makers (Electric)

PROBLEM: Water boils but does not enter coffee basket in percolator-type coffee maker.

EXPLANATION: The perking action in an electric coffee maker is controlled by a floating disc-shaped valve located at the base of the pump tube. If the valve disc fails to close, as might happen when a particle of coffee or coffee residue causes it to jam in its open position, there will be no perking action.

TOOLS AND MATERIALS NEEDED:

(a) a toothpick

(b) baking soda

SOLUTION:

NOTE: Make certain that the pump tube is fully seated in the heater well before each use. (*Figure 1*)

1. Inspect the heater well to see that it is free of anything that might prevent the pump tube from seating fully. (*Figure 2*)

FIG.1

COFFEE BASKET

PUMP TUBE

HEATER WELL

COFFEE STRENGTH CONTROL KNOB

INDICATOR LAMP

2. Inspect the base of the pump tube. If it is distorted or dented, replace the pump tube. This part can be purchased from any appliance service shop. Make certain an exact replacement is used.

3. If the base of the pump tube is not distorted or dented, proceed to check the pump valve.

4. Hold the pump tube in a vertical position and shake it up and down. If free, the valve disc can be heard to clatter.

5. If the valve disc does not clatter, poke it up and down with the tip of a toothpick. If the valve disc does not move freely, examine the pump tube base carefully for coffee residue or a particle of ground coffee that may be jamming the valve disc. Pick clean with the tip of a toothpick the area round the valve disc until the valve moves freely. (*Figure 3*)

SPECIAL NOTE: An accumulation of coffee residue can be removed and prevented by soaking the appliance in dishwashing detergent regularly and boiling with baking soda solution periodically.

FIG.2

HEATER WELL

PUMP TUBE

FIG.3

TOOTH PICK

PUMP TUBE BASE

VALVE DISC

Problem Solver #20

APPLIANCE: Coffee Makers (Electric)

PROBLEM: Coffee is too weak or too strong for desired setting.

EXPLANATION: Many factors are involved in controlling the strength of percolated coffee. The most important points to consider are proportion of coffee and water used, temperature of the water, and the length of perking time.

TOOLS AND MATERIALS NEEDED:

(a) a screwdriver

(b) a toothpick

SOLUTION:

1. Check the directions on the can of your brand of coffee for the correct coffee measurement. Use an accurate measuring utensil.

2. Fill the coffee maker with water to the proper cup level for quantity of coffee used.

    NOTE: Always use water at tap temperature (50°-70° F.). Never use hot water to start the coffee. Pre-heated water will cause the perking action to stop too soon, thus producing weak coffee.

3. If all of the above precautions have been taken and the coffee is still too weak, check the valve disc located in the base of the pump tube. When the valve disc fails to close completely, insufficient perking action results. Clean the areas directly above and below the valve disc of any coffee residue that could prevent the valve disc from moving freely. (*Figure 1*)

4. Check the pump tube base to see that it seats fully into the heater well. If the base of the pump tube is dented or distorted, replace the pump tube. This part may be purchased from appliance parts and service shops.

FIG.1

HEATER WELL

COFFEE STRENGTH
CONTROL KNOB

INDICATOR LAMP

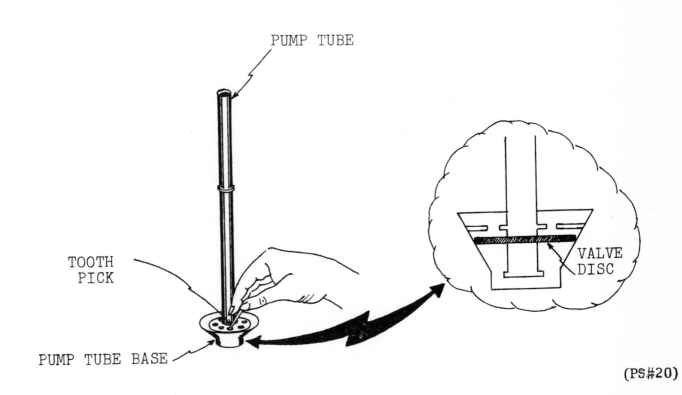

PUMP TUBE

TOOTH
PICK

PUMP TUBE BASE

VALVE
DISC

(PS#20)

SPECIAL NOTE: The length of perking time is automatically controlled by a thermostat. Different coffee blends packaged under different brand labels may require slightly different settings of the coffee strength control knob to suit individual tastes. If, however, the coffee produced is excessively weak (no flavor or color) or excessively strong (bitter), it would indicate that the thermostat is not functioning correctly. The steps that follow list the procedures for uncovering the thermostat and the visual clues that help in evaluating the working condition of the thermostat.

CAUTION: Remove appliance plug from maker before proceeding.

5. Remove the coffee strength control knob by pulling it off, and remove the screw (or screws) that fastens the base section to the pot. Carefully take off the base. (*Figure 2*)

CAUTION: The base section of completely immersible coffee makers should be disassembled by a qualified appliance technician in order to guarantee waterproof assembly.

6. Inspect the wires that are routed to and around the movable thermostat blade. (*Figure 3*) Wires that lie against the blade could prevent its free movement during operation. Move the wires aside.

7. Inspect the thermostat blade and its electrical contact points for corrosion and/or stuck condition. Reassemble coffee maker and test.

NOTE: Water seepage into the base section of the pot (due to leaks or improper cleaning techniques) will cause the thermostat and other working parts to corrode and malfunction. If this condition exists, the coffee maker should be taken to an authorized appliance service shop for repair.

SPECIAL NOTE: To insure satisfactory service from your coffee maker:

A. Carefully follow the manufacturer's instructions on use and care.

B. Do not allow water or coffee spills to run into the base section of the pot.

C. Have qualified service technicians investigate the slightest evidence of coffee leakage into base section as quickly as possible to avoid further damage.

FIG.2

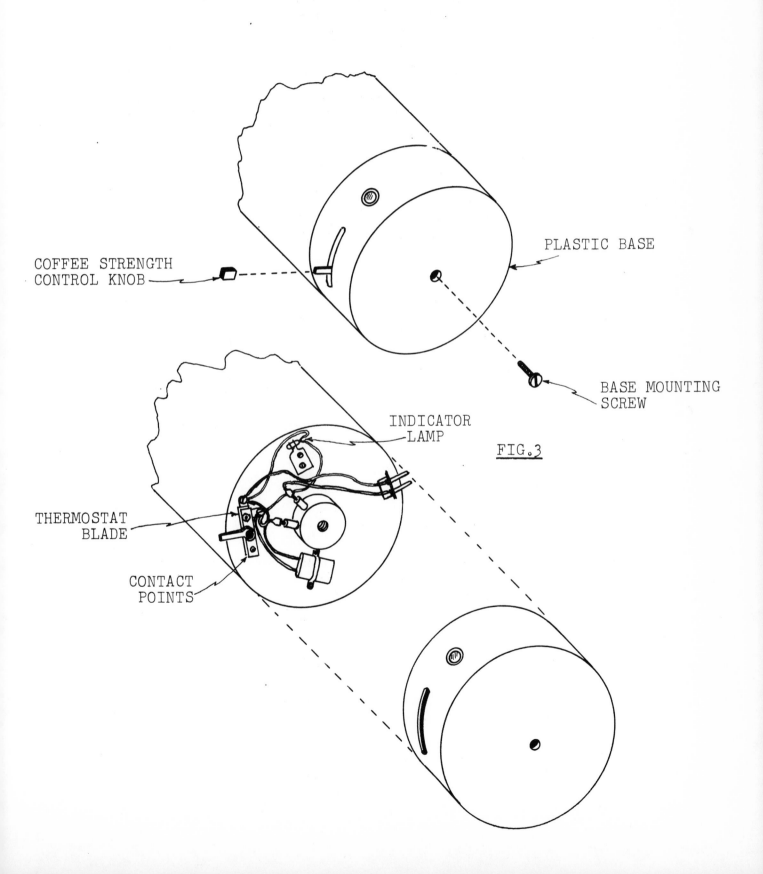

COFFEE STRENGTH
CONTROL KNOB

PLASTIC BASE

BASE MOUNTING
SCREW

INDICATOR
LAMP

FIG.3

THERMOSTAT
BLADE

CONTACT
POINTS

Problem Solver #21

APPLIANCE: Coffee Makers (Electric)

PROBLEM: **Lid falls off when user pours coffee.**

EXPLANATION: The lid of most coffee makers is held firmly on top of the pot by a number of small bumps which protrude around the edge of the lid. Through normal use these bumps can become worn or flattened so that they no longer exert the correct pressure against the pot to hold the lid firmly in place.

TOOLS AND MATERIALS NEEDED:

    (a) a hammer

    (b) a block of wood

    (c) a sardine can opener (key)

SOLUTION:

1. Remove the lid from the coffee maker. (*Figure 1*)

2. Take off the glass lid knob to avoid damaging it. Glass lid knobs are removed by twisting them counter-clockwise and lifting them out.

   NOTE: If the knob is stuck or otherwise difficult to remove, allow knob to remain but be careful not to break it.

3. Place lid on wood block with lid bump contacting wood. (*Figure 2*)

FIG.1

GLASS LID KNOB

LID

FIG.2

LID

LID BUMPS

WOOD BLOCK

4. Place tip of sardine can opener into lid bump cavity and tap the top of can opener with hammer. (*Figure 3*)

   NOTE: Examine the lid bump after tapping to determine how far bump has been extended. In most cases, the lid bumps need be extended only slightly to restore correct lid fit.

5. Rotate lid and tap out remaining lid bumps. Test fit of lid after tapping each lid bump so as to prevent making the lid fit too tightly.

6. If lid is too tight, flatten bumps *slightly* by tapping them with wood block. (*Figure 4*)

Problem Solver #22

APPLIANCE: Coffee Makers (Electric)

PROBLEM: Indicator lamp does not operate.

EXPLANATION: In some coffee percolators, a small red lens lights up to indicate that percolation has stopped and the coffee is ready. The lens light is provided by a small lamp located directly behind the lens. If the percolator works satisfactorily but the lamp fails to indicate, the fault can be corrected by simply replacing the lamp. This is an inexpensive repair and can usually be completed at an appliance repair shop while you wait. However, the procedure for replacing the indicator lamp is described below for those who decide to do it themselves.

FIG.3

SARDINE CAN
OPENER

FIG.4

WOOD BLOCK

LID BUMP

LID

TOOLS AND MATERIALS NEEDED:

(a) a screwdriver

(b) a pair of pliers

CAUTION: Disconnect appliance plug from coffee maker.

SOLUTION:

1. Remove the coffee strength selector knob by pulling it straight off.

2. Remove the screw (or screws) used to fasten the plastic base of the percolator to the pot and carefully take off the base. (*Figure 1*)

3. Locate and identify the indicator lamp.

    NOTE: Two basic types of lamps are presently in use: incandescent lamps and neon lamps. The incandescent lamps resemble the kind of lamp used in flashlights and are usually found in older percolator models. This type is secured in the lamp socket in one of two ways. One is screwed into the socket and is referred to as a screw-base lamp. The other is pushed into the socket and twisted. Two little pins on its base secure this second lamp in the socket. This is known as a bayonet lamp. The neon lamp is more often found in newer model percolators. This lamp does not require a lamp socket. It is connected to the electric wiring of the percolator by two thin wire leads.

4. If a screw-base incandescent lamp is used, remove it from its socket by turning it counter-clockwise. Take the burned out lamp to the nearest appliance repair shop and ask for a replacement.

    NOTE: A qualified appliance technician can usually identify the lamp to be replaced by numbers printed on its base and other code marks. It is a good idea to take along also the manufacturer's name and the model number of the percolator to insure purchase of the correct replacement lamp. (*Figure 1*)

    CAUTION: Before replacing plastic base, make certain that the lamp is correctly aligned behind red lens. The lamp socket bracket may be bent slightly if necessary.

5. To remove bayonet lamp, hold the lamp socket with one hand to prevent it from being forced out of position. Grasp the lamp with the other hand, push into the socket, and twist it counter-clockwise. The lamp can then be pulled straight out of the socket. (*Figure 2*)

FIG.1

SCREW-IN TYPE BULB ASSEMBLY

BASE(REMOVED)

FIG.2

SOCKET

BAYONET TYPE LAMP(REMOVED)

6. To install a replacement bayonet lamp, align the two pins on the base of the lamp with the two channels on the lamp socket. Press the lamp into the base as far as it will go, twist the lamp clockwise, and release it.

7. Align the lamp socket so that the lamp will be positioned directly behind the red lens. Replace the plastic base and secure it to the pot with screw (or screws).

8. If neon lamp is used, check first to see that the lead wires of the lamp are securely connected to their terminals. (*Figure 3*)

   NOTE: Neon lamps do not as a rule burn out. Unless the glass bulb actually breaks, failure of these lamps to operate can usually be traced to broken or loose wire leads. These lamps are purchased and replaced as an entire assembly that can include lamp, insulating sleeves, terminals, and in some models an additional part called a resistor. (*Figure 3A*)

FIG.3

NEON TYPE LAMP

FIG.3A

RESISTOR

NEON LAMP ASSEMBLY
(REMOVED)

9. To replace neon lamp assembly, loosen terminal screws or nuts by turning counter-clockwise about two full turns and remove the lamp lead terminals. This will release the lamp assembly. (*Figure 4*)

   NOTE: In some models the lamp is held in position behind the lens by a small clamp. If so, slip the lamp out of the clamp to release it.

10. To install new lamp assembly, place lead wire terminal under terminal screws (or nuts) and tighten securely. Place lamp under clamp. (*Figure 5*)

   CAUTION: Make certain that wire leads of clamp are positioned away from other parts. Handle lamp wires carefully to prevent them from breaking. Do not bend them sharply or tug them too hard.

11. Secure plastic base to pot with screw (screws) and replace coffee strength control knob.

LAMP BRACKET

NEON LAMP

FIG.4

RESISTOR

CLAMP

TERMINAL SCREWS

NEON LAMP MOUNTED AND
CONNECTED

CLAMP

FIG.5

Problem Solver #23

APPLIANCE: Vaporizers

PROBLEM: House lights dim or fuse blows when vaporizer is plugged into wall outlet.

EXPLANATION: When any appliance causes house lights to dim, it should serve as a warning that more electric power is being demanded than can be supplied by the electric line. This can happen when too many appliances are connected to the same electric line or when the appliance itself is not working properly. A blown fuse or tripped circuit breaker (when used) serves as fairly reliable evidence that the power demand has exceeded the safety limit.

TOOLS AND MATERIALS NEEDED:

(a) instructional literature (supplied by manufacturer)

(b) a long-handled spoon

SOLUTION: 1. Check for and disconnect other heavy wattage appliances operating in the same room or on the same electric line. If lights still dim or fuse blows again, follow procedure outlined below.

2. Read and carefully follow manufacturer's instructions on use of vaporizer.

NOTE: Modern vaporizers depend upon a saline (salt and water) solution for operation. When the proportion of salt added is too great, a vaporizer will draw an excessive amount of electricity. This can cause lights to dim and/or a fuse to blow.

3. Spill out contents of vaporizer and refill with fresh clear water.

4. Add *correct* amount of salt to water and stir with spoon to dissolve all salt. (*Figure 1*)

5. Plug unit into wall outlet and allow at least two minutes for steam vapor to appear.

CAUTION: Do not add more salt to hasten or increase steam vapor. Also do not add medication to the water. Most vaporizers contain a special well near the steam spout for any medication. (*Figure 1*)

FIG.1

MEDICATION WELL

STEAM SPOUT

CORRECT
AMOUNT OF
SALT

WATER LEVEL

Problem Solver #24

APPLIANCE: Vaporizers

PROBLEM: Vaporizer produces little or no steam.

EXPLANATION: The simpler of two causes of this problem is improper filling and preparation of the vaporizer. The second and more serious cause develops over a period of time through normal use and requires the cleaning or replacement of two electrodes that produce the steam.

TOOLS AND MATERIALS NEEDED:

(a) instructional literature (supplied by manufacturer)

(b) a small phillips screwdriver

(c) a medium size screwdriver (flatblade)

(d) two emery boards (used for fingernails)

(e) a long-handled spoon

(f) a pair of pliers

SOLUTION: 1. Read and carefully follow manufacturer's instructions on use of vaporizer.

NOTE: For satisfactory operation, vaporizers depend upon a correct proportion of salt and water. When not enough salt is used, vaporizers will not produce a sufficient quantity of steam. It is wise, therefore, to make sure that the manufacturer's recommended quantity of salt is carefully measured.

2. Spill out contents of vaporizer and refill with fresh clear water.

3. Add *correct* amount of salt to water and stir with spoon to make certain all salt is dissolved.

4. Plug unit into wall outlet and allow at least two minutes for steam vapor to appear.

CAUTION: Do not add more salt to hasten or increase steam vapor. If vaporizer still does not produce enough steam, proceed to solution steps below.

FIG.1

STEAM SPOUT

MEDICATION WELL

STEAM CHAMBER

WATER STORAGE JAR

WATER LEVEL

5. Disconnect vaporizer from wall outlet.

6. Remove vaporizer steam chamber from the water jar. (*Figure 1*) Allow water to drain from steam chamber into water jar.

7. Remove the screws that fasten the steam chamber cover. (*Figure 2*)

8. Examine the electrodes. They will probably be encrusted with heavy deposits of minerals and salt. (*Figure 3*)

9. Carefully scrape off mineral deposits with an emery board until metal electrodes are thoroughly clean. (*Figure 4*)

CAUTION AND NOTE: Take care when cleaning electrodes not to disturb or break the ceramic insulator that separates the two electrodes. The metal electrodes must never touch each other. Cleaning of electrodes is usually all that is required to restore proper steam supply. However, if examination of electrodes shows that large portions of the electrodes have been eaten away by corrosion, the electrodes must then be replaced.

SPECIAL NOTE: In most vaporizers, the electrodes are the only "working" parts. Replacing the electrodes with new ones can restore the operation of a vaporizer to "like new" condition. The procedure for replacing the electrodes is outlined in the steps that follow.

FIG.2

MOUNTING SCREWS

STEAM CHAMBER

FIG.3

ELECTRODES

STEAM CHAMBER COVER

MOUNTING SCREWS

FIG.4

CERAMIC
INSULATOR

ELECTRODES

EMERY
BOARD

10. Remove the screws that fasten the terminal cover plate and lift off the cover plate. (*Figure 5*)

11. Remove the terminal nuts (turn counter-clockwise) with a pair of pliers. (*Figure 6*)

12. Lift the line cord terminal connectors off the threaded terminal screws. Remove the two washers and set them carefully aside for reuse with new electrodes. (*Figure 6*)

13. Grasp electrodes and remove them by pulling them straight out.

14. Insert new replacement electrodes in the same position as original ones. Make certain the two neoprene seals (*Figure 6*) are in place and are seated correctly to prevent water and steam from entering the electrical terminal compartment. Broken or worn seals should be replaced. These may be purchased at an authorized service center.

15. Hold electrodes in position and replace washers. Replace line cord terminal connectors. Thread terminal nuts down and tighten them with pliers. Make sure that terminal connectors do not touch each other.

16. Replace terminal cover plate and steam chamber cover to complete the repair.

FIG.5

MEDICATION WELL

TERMINAL
COVER

FIG.6

TERMINAL NUTS

LINE CORD
TERMINALS

NEOPRENE SEALS

CERAMIC INSULATOR

ELECTRODES

Problem Solver #25

APPLIANCE: Electric Fry Pans and Cookers

PROBLEM: **Appliance does not heat.**

EXPLANATION: Modern fry pans and cookers are constructed so that they have two major working sections. These are: (1) the pan (or pot), which contains the heating element; and (2) the control unit, which contains the thermostat and, on some models, an indicator lamp. When this type of appliance does not heat, the cause must be traced to one of the two sections. Once the malfunctioning section has been identified, the repair is best completed by replacing the entire section.

TOOLS AND MATERIALS NEEDED:

    (a) a table lamp (with 40 watt bulb or less)

    (b) 6-foot extension cord

    (c) a handful of fine steel wool
       (or abrasive cleaning pad)

    (d) a paring knife

SOLUTION: 1. Disconnect control unit from the pan (or pot) and examine the terminal pins for signs of discoloration or corrosion. (*Figure 1*)

       2. If terminal pins are found to be discolored or corroded, clean them with steel wool. Retest pan to see if it heats. If appliance still fails to heat, proceed to the test outlined on the following pages.

FIG.1

PAN

TERMINAL PINS

CONTROL UNIT

SPECIAL NOTE: A simple testing circuit can be arranged with any available table lamp and a 6-foot extension cord. This testing circuit will provide an effective visual indication that can be used to determine which of the two sections (pan or control unit) is defective. The procedure for arranging and using the test circuit is outlined in the following steps.

3. Separate the wires of the extension cord for about ten inches along the center of its length by slitting them with a sharp paring knife. (*Figure 2*) Guide the paring knife carefully along the insulated center of the extension cord in order to avoid exposing the copper wire.

4. Cut through one side of the separate extension cord wires with the paring knife. (*Figure 3*)

5. Remove about an inch of insulation from the cut wire ends. (*Figure 4*)

FIG.2

EXTENSION CORD
SOCKET

EXTENSION CORD

FIG.3

FIG.4

TEST LEAD ENDS

6. Wrap the cut wire ends of the extension cord around each terminal pin on the pan. (*Figure 5*)

7. Screw a small wattage bulb (40 watts or less) into the lamp. Connect the lamp plug into the extension cord receptacle. Connect the extension cord plug into a convenient wall outlet. (*Figure 5*)

8. Turn the lamp switch on. If lamp does not light, it means that the heating element in the pan is not working.

   NOTE: The heating element is usually embedded in the casting of the pan or pot and cannot be removed. Replacement, therefore, will require the purchase of a new pan or pot. This section can be purchased at any appliance repair shop.

9. If the lamp lights, it means that the heating element is working and that the malfunction is in the control unit.

   NOTE: Because of the exacting tolerances within which the control unit must operate, service and repairs to this unit should be performed only by a qualified appliance technician.

FIG.5

TABLE LAMP

EXTENSION CORD

PAN

TERMINAL PINS

Problem Solver #26

APPLIANCE: Electric Deep Fryers; Fry Pans (Not Teflon Coated)

PROBLEM: **Pan-fried food sticks and/or burns at prescribed settings.**

EXPLANATION: This complaint usually indicates that the surface temperature of the pan is too high. This can occur when the thermostat located in the control unit of the appliance becomes defective. However, since other factors may also contribute to the burning of food, the operation of the thermostat should be tested before it is unnecessarily condemned and replaced.

TOOLS AND MATERIALS NEEDED:

(a) a dial thermometer
(used for candymaking and deep frying)

SOLUTION:

NOTE: Two methods of testing the operation of the thermostat will be described in the steps that follow. The first method can be used on deep fryers that have an indicating lamp. The second method can be employed with those that do not have an indicating lamp.

1. Pour about two inches of water into the pot.

2. Turn the temperature control knob to its highest setting (400° F.) and allow the water to come to a rolling boil. (*Figure 1*)

3. Allow water to continue to boil for about three minutes. Then turn control knob slowly back toward the lower temperature settings until indicator light goes out.

4. Stop turning the knob when the indicator lamp goes out and read the temperature that the knob points to on the dial.

FIG.1

FRY BASKET

INDICATOR LAMP

TEMPERATURE CONTROL KNOB SET TO 400°

5. If the knob points to a temperature between 190° and 230° F., you can assume that the thermostat is functioning correctly. If the light does not go out or if the knob points to a temperature that is not between the range given above, it means that the thermostat control unit is defective and must be repaired or replaced. The appliance should be taken to an appliance repair shop for further testing and service.

6. To test the thermostat control unit for fry pans and/or cookers that do not have an indicator lamp, pour at least two inches of clear cooking oil into pan or pot and set the temperature control knob to 300° F. (*Figure 2*)

7. Connect line cord plug into wall outlet and allow oil to heat for at least six minutes.

8. Place a dial thermometer (used for candymaking or deep frying) into the oil and measure the temperature. (*Figure 3*)

   CAUTION: Make sure sensitive stem portion of thermometer is immersed at least two inches into the heated oil.

9. If the thermometer reading is between 270° and 330° F., it means that the thermostat control unit is functioning properly.

10. If the thermometer reading is less than 270° F. or more than 330° F., it means that the thermostat control unit is defective and should be taken to an appliance repair shop for service.

    SPECIAL NOTE: Cooking oil, shortening, and butter behave differently when used for frying. Some of these products contain a large quantity of food solids that produce smoke at high frying temperatures. This condition is often mistakenly thought to be caused by defective operation of the pan or cooker. Selection of oil or shortening that has been refined for frying can eliminate unnecessary smoke.

FIG.2

TEMPERATURE CONTROL KNOB
SET TO 300

FIG.3

CORRECT TEMPERATURE RANGE
FOR 300 CONTROL SETTING

Problem Solver #27

APPLIANCE: Teflon Coated Electric Fry Pans and Cookers

PROBLEM: **Teflon coating is deteriorating.**

EXPLANATION: Teflon is the modern plastic material used to coat the inside surface of pots and pans for a no-stick surface. When properly cared for, the Teflon coating can last the life of the pan or cooker. If abused, the coating can be ruined.

TOOLS AND MATERIALS NEEDED:

(a) manufacturer's use and care literature

SOLUTION: Read and carefully follow manufacturer's instructions on the use and care of Teflon coated pans and cookers.

SPECIAL NOTE: Preventive care is the only solution for preventing damage or further deterioration of the Teflon coating. The first products employing Teflon were often coated too thinly to withstand even normal use. Special plastic utensils had to be used to protect the Teflon coating from damage. Owners of these products were cautioned by the manufacturer to avoid using metal utensils to stir cooking ingredients. Many people continued to use metal utensils. This practice invariably resulted in portions of the Teflon coating being scratched or chipped away. However, recent improvements and moderate care should insure the effectiveness of the Teflon coating for the life of the product. Moreover, some manufacturers now claim that ordinary metal utensils may be used with the Teflon coating without fear of damage.

The following precautions are offered for prolonging the effectiveness of Teflon coatings used in electric cookers.

1. Avoid the use of sharp metal utensils for stirring or scraping.

2. Avoid the use of abrasive cleaning pads.

3. Never allow an empty pan or pot to heat to high temperatures. This can scorch the Teflon coating and cause it to discolor and deteriorate.

FIG.1

TEFLON COATING

PLASTIC UTENSIL

ELECTRIC FRY PAN

Problem Solver #28

APPLIANCE: Electric Sandwich Grill and Waffle Baker
               (Not Teflon Coated)

PROBLEM: **Waffles stick to grill.**

EXPLANATION: Removing a waffle that has stuck to the hot grills of a
               waffle baker can be a nuisance and a hazard. The secret
               of how to prevent this from happening lies in the
               preparation and cleaning care of the surfaces of the
               grills.

TOOLS AND MATERIALS NEEDED:

     (a) scouring pad

     (b) clear, light cooking oil (nonsmoking type)

     (c) basting brush

     (d) paper towels

SOLUTION: 1. Allow waffle baker to cool to room temperature
                  before attempting to handle grill sections.

               2. Clean grill surfaces carefully with scouring pad.
                  Make certain all burned-on waffle residue is re-
                  moved. (*Figure 1*)

               3. Rinse grills thoroughly with warm water. Make
                  sure all traces of cleaning agent (soap or deter-
                  gent) are removed. (*Figure 2*)

FIG.1

WAFFLE BAKER
GRILL

SCOURING PAD

FIG.2

WET RAG (RINSE)

CAUTION: Do not hold grill under running water since there is danger that some water may get into the area below the base and come into contact with electrical connections. Use a wet cloth or rag to rinse.

4. Dry the grills thoroughly with a clean cloth or towel.

5. Apply a nonsmoking cooking oil to the baking surfaces of the grills with a basting brush. Make certain that the surfaces are completely coated. (*Figure 3*)

6. Wipe the surfaces of the grills with paper towels until all excess oil has been absorbed. (*Figure 4*)

7. Waffle baker is now ready for use.

SPECIAL NOTE: Waffle grills are especially designed with finely pitted surfaces. The pitting acts much like very small wells that can store small quantities of cooking oil evenly over the entire surfaces of the grills.

Once the surfaces of the grills have been treated as described above, the waffle baker can be used continuously without further need for oiling the surfaces. In between use, the surfaces need only to be wiped clean with dry towels and should not be cleaned with detergents or scouring pads.

If, however, an occasional cleaning becomes necessary, as would be the case after a long period of storage, the cleaning and treatment as described in the solution steps 1 through 7 should be followed.

FIG.3

BASTING BRUSH

GRILL

LIGHT COOKING OIL

FIG.4

PAPER TOWEL

Problem Solver #29

APPLIANCE: Electric Sandwich Grill and Waffle Baker

PROBLEM: **No heat on one or both waffle grills.**

EXPLANATION: Heating element wires are located behind both the top and bottom grills of waffle bakers. In some waffle baker models, the heating element wires of each grill operate independently; therefore, a broken or burned-out element wire in one grill would not prevent the other grill from heating. In other waffle baker models, the heating element wires operate together. In this kind of waffle baker, a break or burn-out in either heating element wire would prevent both grills from heating. However, the solution to the heating problems that may be encountered in either type is the same. The exact point at which the wires have broken or burned apart must be located and repaired.

TOOLS AND MATERIALS NEEDED:

(a) a medium size screwdriver (flatblade)

(b) a pair of long-nose pliers

(c) one 6-32 ¼″ long roundhead brass screw

(d) one 6-32 brass nut

SOLUTION: 1. Remove the line cord plug from the wall outlet.

2. Remove both grills. (*Figures 1 and 2*)

NOTE: Waffle grills are secured to the baker with either screws or clips. (*Figures 1 and 2*)

FIG.1

HEATING ELEMENT WIRE

CERAMIC INSULATOR

CLIP TYPE GRILL FASTENERS

FIG.2

HEATING ELEMENT WIRE

GRILL FASTENING SCREW

3. Examine the heating element wires carefully until the break (point at which wire has parted) is located. (*Figure 3*)

4. Form each wire end into a loop, or eyelet, with long-nose pliers. (*Figure 4*) Each eyelet opening should only be large enough to allow a size 6-32 screw to pass through it freely. Do not form too large an eyelet.

5. Insert the brass screw through both eyelets and secure them by threading the brass nut onto the screw.

6. Hold the nut with the long-nose pliers and tighten the screw securely with a screwdriver. (*Figure 5*)

7. Inspect the heating element wire to make certain that it is supported securely by the ceramic insulators. Also, make certain that the element wire does *not* contact the metal housing of the baker anywhere along its route. Carefully bend the wire away from the metal housing whenever necessary.

8. Replace the grills to complete the repair.

NOTE: Other solutions for the repair and replacement of heating element wire are given in Section II, General Repair Procedures, Heating Element Wire.

FIG.3

ELEMENT WIRE   BREAK POINT

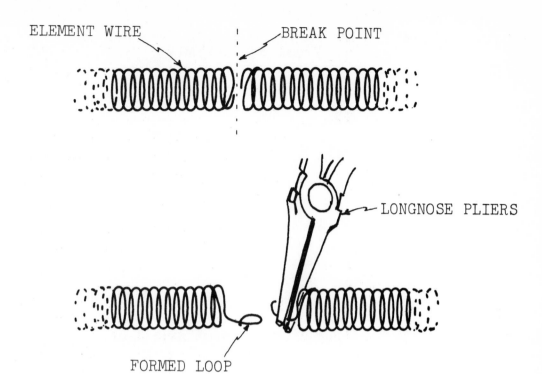

FIG.4

LONGNOSE PLIERS

FORMED LOOP

BRASS SCREW

BRASS NUT

FIG.5

SCREWDRIVER

LONGNOSE PLIERS

Problem Solver #30

APPLIANCE: Space Heaters (All Types)

PROBLEM: **Plug becomes excessively hot.**

EXPLANATION: Space heaters require large quantities of electric power over long operating periods. It is not uncommon to operate this appliance continuously throughout a night or day. Extra care, therefore, must be taken to insure perfect electrical contact between the appliance and its source of power. An overheated plug is an indication that a poor connection exists at the wall outlet. Moreover, it represents a potential fire hazard and should be eliminated as quickly as possible.

TOOLS AND MATERIALS NEEDED:

    (a) a medium size screwdriver (flatblade)

    (b) a sharp paring or pocket knife

    (c) one two-prong male plug
       (heavy-duty, rubber appliance type)

SOLUTION: 1. Remove the line cord plug from the wall outlet.

               2. Examine the plug. Check to see that the prongs are firmly attached to the plug body. (*Figure 1*) If the plug prongs wiggle freely or if the plug body shows signs of charring (deterioration due to heat), the plug should be replaced. Refer to Section II, General Repair Procedures, Plugs, for complete replacement procedure.

TWO DIFFERENT MODELS OF SPACE HEATERS

NOTE: ALTHOUGH DESIGN OF HEATER
      MAY CHANGE, OPERATING
      PRINCIPLES REMAIN THE SAME.

FIG.1

PLUG BODY

PLUG PRONGS

3. If the plug prongs are firmly attached and the plug body does not show signs of heat damage, check the fit of the plug in the wall outlet for looseness.

NOTE: Firm pressure should be required to insert and remove the plug from the wall outlet.

4. If the plug shows evidence of looseness, spread both prongs of the plug slightly by inserting the flat blade of a screwdriver between the folded layers of each prong. (*Figure 2*)

SPECIAL NOTE: A loose fit can be caused by either the plug or a worn-out wall outlet receptacle. Some appliances have been originally equipped with plugs having prongs fashioned from folded strips of metal. When new, the folded type prongs have the necessary thickness to insure good contact with the wall outlet receptacle. With use, however, the folded metal prongs become flattened, and looseness results. If the plug still fits loosely after the prongs have been spread, it can be assumed that the wall outlet receptacle is worn and should be replaced.

NOTE: Most local electrical codes state that house wiring, wall outlets, and electrical fixtures must be installed and repaired by licensed electricians.

FIG.2

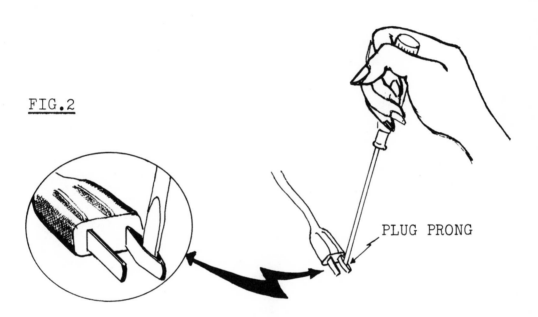

PLUG PRONG

Problem Solver #31

APPLIANCE: Space Heaters (Reflector Type)

PROBLEM: **Heating element glows red, but not enough heat can be felt.**

EXPLANATION: Space heaters are used normally to supplement the existing heating system. Their effectiveness depends upon their ability to throw heat into a small space or section of a larger area that requires additional heat. The reflector space heater moves heat into a space by reflecting the heat produced by the heating element. This heater cannot operate efficiently if the chromed surface of its reflector has become clouded with dust or dirt.

TOOLS AND MATERIALS NEEDED:

(a) two soft rags

(b) commercial metal polish

(c) a flatblade screwdriver (medium size)

SOLUTION: 1. Remove the plug from the wall outlet.

NOTE: *Figures 1 and 3* illustrate two typical reflector space heaters.

2. Remove the front guard. (*Figures 2 and 4*)

3. To remove the front guard of the space heater (*Figure 1*), grasp the front guard close to where the guardrail ends are inserted into holes in the edge of the bowl reflector. Bend the guard until the rail ends are removed from the holes. (*Figure 2*)

FIG.1

GUARD RAIL ENDS

FRONT GUARD

FIG.2

GUARDRAIL ENDS

GUARD RAIL MOUNTING HOLES

FRONT
GUARD
(REMOVED)

POLISHED
REFLECTOR

4. To remove the front guard of the space heater (*Figure 3*), remove two screws located in the lower corners of the guard. (*Figure 4*) Tilt the top cover back slightly and lift out the guard.

5. Clean and polish the reflector with metal polish applied to a soft rag. Use a dry soft rag to remove all traces of the metal polish.

CAUTION: When cleaning the reflector of the kind of space heater shown in *Figure 3*, take care not to press against the heating element wires.

Problem Solver #32

APPLIANCE: Space Heaters

PROBLEM: **The heater does not heat.**

EXPLANATION: In space heaters, as in other heat-producing appliances, heat is produced by the effect of an electric current passing through the heating element wire. When the electric current is prevented either from reaching the heating element wire or from passing completely through it, the space heater will fail to operate. The flow of electricity is stopped when a house fuse is blown or when a component of the space heater becomes defective.

TOOLS AND MATERIALS NEEDED:

(a) a flatblade screwdriver (medium size)

(b) a pair of long-nose pliers

(c) a tube of graphite lubricant

FIG.3

FRONT GUARD

FIG.4

FRONT GUARD
(REMOVED)

FRONT
GUARD
MOUNTING
SCREW

FRONT GUARD MOUNTING SCREW

SOLUTION:

1. Make certain that the wall outlet has electric power. Plug a lamp or other appliance known to be in good working order into the outlet used for the space heater. If the lamp or other appliance fails to operate, it can be assumed that a fuse has blown or that a circuit breaker has tripped off, thus preventing electric power from reaching the wall outlet, or that the wall outlet itself is defective. Refer to Section II, General Repair Procedures, Fuses and Circuit Breakers, for further instructions about this condition. If, however, the lamp or other appliance used for testing the wall outlet operates, it means that the problem is in the space heater.

2. Examine the line cord plug. Check the plug prongs for looseness. Test the condition of the line cord wires going into the plug by tugging firmly on the plug against the line cord. (*Figure 1*) If the plug prongs wiggle freely or if the plug parts from this line cord when pulled upon, the plug should be replaced. See Section II, General Repair Procedures, Plugs, for further information.

    SPECIAL NOTE: Many space heater models employ a safety switch that shuts the space heater off automatically if it is tipped over. (*Figure 2* illustrates such a safety switch.) Whenever the space heater is used, the safety switch should be checked to see that it is functioning properly.

3. Examine the operation of the safety switch. Place the heater on a table so that the switch is at eye level. Check to see that the contact points come together (close) when the heater rests on the table and that they part (open) when the heater is lifted off the table.

FIG.1

LINE CORD

PLUG   PLUG PRONGS

FIG.2

FRONT GUARD
(REMOVED)

FRONT
GUARD
SCREW

SAFETY
SWITCH(ENLARGED)

POINTS

PUSH UP TO
CLOSE POINTS

SAFETY SWITCH CONTROL
SHAFT

FRONT
GUARD
SCREW

4. If the contact points of the switch do not close when the heater rests on its stand, check the switch control shaft to see that it moves up and down freely.

5. Operate the switch control shaft by pushing it up manually. The control shaft should move up freely and then return to its lower position automatically.

6. If the switch control shaft does not move freely, coat the shaft with graphite lubricant sprayed from a plastic dispenser. (*Figure 3*)

7. If the switch control shaft moves up and down freely, but the contacts do not come together when the heater is rested on its stand, it means that the switch control shaft is not extending up far enough to move the contact points together.

8. Check to see that the switch control shaft extends down to the table surface far enough to be lifted when the heater is resting on its stand. If the shaft is not lifted sufficiently, bend the heater stand slightly by pressing down on both ends. (*Figure 4*) This should allow the shaft to protrude further past the heater stand for proper operation.

FIG.3

SWITCH CONTROL
SHAFT

GRAPHITE

GRAPHITE
DISPENSER

FIG.4

HEATER STAND

9. If examination of the safety switch proves that it is functioning properly but the heater still does not operate, check the terminal connectors of the heater element wire and the element wire itself to see that there are no loose connections or broken wires. (*Figure 5*)

10. Remove the front guard by removing the two screws located at both lower corners of the heater. (*Figure 2*) Lift up the top of the heater and lift out the front guard.

11. Grasp each connector and wiggle it to check for looseness. Replace any connector that feels loose. Refer to Section II, General Repair Procedures, Terminal and Wire Connectors, for complete instructions.

   NOTE: The type of heating element wire used in the space heater shown in *Figure 5* is assembled in the factory as a complete unit. This type of heater element cannot be repaired practically. When broken (burned out), this heater element must be purchased and replaced as an entire unit. The procedure for replacing the heating element is given in the steps that follow.

FIG.5

TOP
MOUNTING
BRACKET

HEATING
ELEMENT
UNIT

POLISHED
CHROME
REFLECTOR

TERMINAL
CONNECTORS

BOTTOM MOUNTING
BRACKET

12. Grasp the lower retaining (horseshoe-shaped) clip with a pair of long-nose pliers and pull it off the heater element mounting shaft. (*Figure 6*)

13. Disconnect the heater element by grasping the terminal connectors manually and pulling them off the terminals. (*Figure 6*)

14. Grasp the heating element unit by the mounting rod and lift the entire heater unit up and out of the bottom mounting bracket. Slide the heating unit out of the top mounting bracket to free it completely. (*Figure 7*)

    NOTE: An exact replacement heating element unit may be purchased from an authorized appliance service shop.

15. Install the new replacement heater element unit by *reversing* the procedures in steps 12 through 14 above.

FIG.6

TERMINAL
CONNECTORS

RETAINING CLIP

LONG NOSE PLIERS

FIG.7

RETAINING CLIP
(REMOVED)

NOTE: The space heater illustrated in *Figure* 8 does not employ a safety switch. When this type of space heater fails to operate, the heating element unit should be checked. The steps that follow describe the procedure for checking, repairing, and/or replacing the heater element.

16. Disconnect the line cord plug from the wall outlet.

17. Grasp the heating element and unscrew it (by turning it counter-clockwise) from its socket. Inspect the heating element closely at the terminal screws. (*Figure* 9) Check to see that the terminal screws are tight. Turn them in a clockwise direction with a screwdriver.

18. If terminal screw connections appear to be good, carefully inspect the element wire along its entire length on the cone-shaped ceramic form.

19. If heating element wire is found to be parted (burned-out or broken), replace the entire heating element.

    NOTE: This type of heating element is usually readily available from any appliance repair shop.

FIG.8

POLISHED REFLECTOR

FIG.9

HEATING ELEMENT UNIT

SOCKET

TERMINAL SCREWS

Section II

General Repair Procedures

#33 Fuses and Circuit Breakers

How To: Locate and replace a blown fuse.

Explanation: Fuses are safety devices. Their purpose is to protect electrical equipment (appliances) and the electrical house wires from damage. When a fuse blows, it is an indication that the demand for electric power has exceeded the safe carrying capacity of the electric supply line. A fuse contains a short metal link through which all of the electric power in a supply line must flow. The metal link is designed to melt apart when the electric power flowing through it is excessive and generates more heat than the metal fuse link can withstand. The types of fuses most commonly found in home use are constructed with a screw base and are called plug fuses. There are three common varieties of plug fuses: (1) standard base; (2) standard base, time delay; and (3) tamperproof (fusestat). (*Figure 1*) Time delay fuses are designed to withstand short periods of excessive electric power draw without blowing. This feature is especially useful in house circuits that supply motor-driven appliances (washing machines, refrigerators, clothes dryers, etc.). The ordinary standard base and tamperproof base fuses are generally adequate for use with heating appliances.

Tools and Materials Needed:

(a) a replacement fuse (same electrical rating—amperes—and type as original)

(b) a flashlight

Steps: 1. When fuse is suspected of having blown, turn off all switches (appliances, lights, etc.) that have stopped operating.

2. Locate fuse box that contains the house fuses. (*Figure 2*)

FIG.1 PLUG TYPE FUSES

STANDARD BASE

STANDARD BASE (TIME DELAY)

TAMPER PROOF

FIG.2 TYPICAL FUSE BOX

DOOR (CLOSED)

SPRING LATCH

DOOR (OPEN)

FUSES

3. Examine the small window of each fuse in the fuse box. Use a flashlight to aid visibility. The window of a blown fuse (or fuses) will usually appear blackened or clouded.

NOTE: Some electric lines use two fuses for protection.

4. Remove the suspect fuse by unscrewing it (counter-clockwise) from its socket.

5. Examine fuse to identify its electrical size and type. Its electrical size (in amperes, or amps) is usually printed on the metal edge surrounding its window and on the small metal contact tip on its base. (*Figure 3*)

NOTE: It is always wise to anticipate the possibility of a fuse blowing and to keep an assortment of replacement fuses available near the fuse box.

6. Select a replacement fuse that is identical to the blown fuse and screw the new fuse (or fuses) into the fuse socket.

NOTE AND CAUTION: Standard base plug fuses are made available in sizes of 5 amps, 10 amps, 15 amps, 20 amps, 25 amps, and 30 amps. Since the screw bases of these fuses are identical, they may accidentally be interchanged. Extreme precautions should be taken to avoid replacing a blown fuse with one which has a higher amp rating. Tamperproof plug fuses are also available in the amps sizes listed above. Their screw base construction, however, does not permit different size fuses to be interchanged since different sized screw bases are provided for each electrical size.

7. After fuses have been replaced, turn on appliances, lights, and other electrical apparatus that had gone dead.

NOTE: If circuit fuse blows again when appliance or other electrical apparatus is turned on, it indicates that the electrical overload is still present and must be disconnected from the power line. In most instances, the faulty appliance or other electrical apparatus can be identified by elimination. This will require a systematic trial of each appliance. If, however, the defective apparatus cannot be isolated after a reasonable effort has been made, a licensed electrician should be called to correct the condition.

FIG.3

FUSE SIZE(IN AMPERES)

PLUG FUSE

BLOWN FUSE

FUSE SIZE(IN AMPERES)

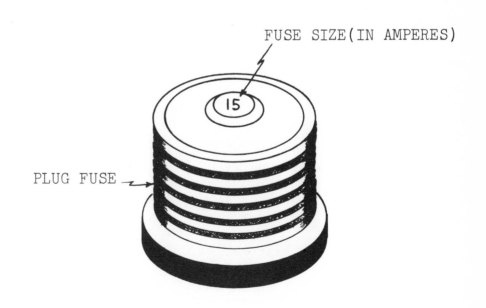

PLUG FUSE

#34 Male Plugs

How To: Replace a two-prong male plug.

Explanation: Many types of male plugs are on the market; however, most are not suitable for use on heat-producing appliances. The type of plug recommended is generally referred to as a "heavy-duty male plug" and is shown in the illustrations.

Tools and Materials Needed:

   (a) a heavy-duty two-prong male plug (available at any electrical hardware store)

   (b) a sharp paring knife

   (c) a flatblade screwdriver (medium size)

Steps: 1. Remove the defective plug by cutting the line cord about one-half inch before the plug; then discard it. This will eliminate any weakened, frayed, or oxidized wire that might interfere with the operation of the new plug. (*Figure 1*)

             2. Remove about three inches of outer insulation (when encountered) by slitting it lengthwise with a sharp knife. (*Figure 2*)

                caution: Take care not to cut through the inner wire insulation.

             3. Remove about one inch of the inner rubber insulation from each wire end. (*Figure 3*)

                caution: Avoid cutting any of the fine wire strands.

FIG.1

CUT OFF PLUG

FIG.2

REMOVE OUTER INSULATION

OUTER INSULATION

CUT HERE

FIG.3

REMOVE INNER INSULATION

BARE WIRE END

INNER INSULATION

4. Feed the wire ends of the remaining prepared line cord through the replacement male plug and tie an "Underwriter's knot" as shown in steps a, b, and c of *Figure 4.*

5. Twist the loose strands of each wire end together tightly. (*Figure 5*)

   CAUTION: Carefully straighten the wire strands before attempting to twist them together to prevent wire strands from puncturing fingers.

6. Pull the Underwriter's knot down into the cavity of the plug.

7. Loosen both terminal screws of the plug, but do not force them beyond their stop points. (*Figure 5*)

8. Bring each line cord wire end around the back of each prong, and wrap the bare wire portion of each end around and under the plug terminal screws in a clockwise direction. (*Figure 6*)

   NOTE: Avoid getting insulation caught under the terminal screws.

9. Cut off any excess wire that protrudes from under the terminal screw heads and tighten the screws with a screwdriver.

   NOTE: Make certain that there are no loose strands of wire that can touch both of the plug prongs and cause a short circuit.

10. Slide the fiber cover plate over the prongs. (*Figure 6*)

FIG.4

A

B

C

FIG.5

INNER INSULATION

OUTER INSULATION

PRONGS

TERMINAL
SCREW

FIG.6

FIBER COVER

#35 Female Plugs

How To: Replace a female appliance plug.

Explanation: Female appliance plugs are used to provide a convenient method of disconnecting the line cord from the appliance. Female appliance plugs vary in size, and some have as many as three cavities. The female plug shown in the illustration is the type commonly used for coffee makers, waffle bakers, and other appliances and is, therefore, more often encountered. Moreover, the steps used to replace this female plug can be applied to all other varieties of this plug.

Tools and Materials Needed:

(a) a sharp paring knife

(b) a female appliance plug
    (available at any electrical hardware store)

(c) a flatblade screwdriver (medium size)

Steps:

1. Cut the defective plug off by cutting the line cord about one-half inch in front of the plug with a sharp paring knife. (*Figure 1*)

2. Take old plug to electrical hardware store and match new replacement plug to it.

3. Remove the screws that fasten the two halves of the new plug together. (*Figure 3*)

   CAUTION: Take care not to drop the two nuts. (*Figure 6*)

4. Remove about three-quarters of an inch of insulation from the line cord wire ends with a sharp knife. (*Figure 2*)

   CAUTION: Do not cut off any strands from wire ends.

5. Twist wire strands together tightly and form each wire end into a hook. (*Figure 3*)

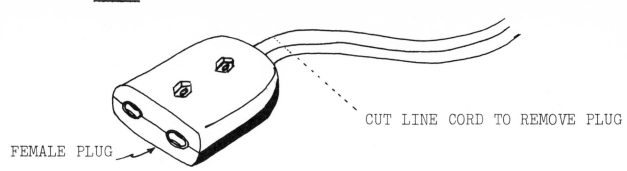

FIG.1

FEMALE PLUG

CUT LINE CORD TO REMOVE PLUG

FIG.2

BARE WIRE END

KNIFE

FIG.3

TERMINAL SCREWS

HOOKED WIRE ENDS

TERMINAL
CONNECTORS

HALF OF NEW PLUG

6. Loosen (do not remove) the two terminal screws located in terminal connectors. (*Figure* 3) Place the hooked wire ends under the terminal screws in a clockwise direction and tighten terminal screws securely. (*Figure 4*)

   CAUTION: Do not overtighten terminal screws. Wire ends may be broken.

7. Place terminal connections into cavities in the plug body. (*Figure 5*)

8. Put other half of plug body in place and put plug body together with nuts and fastening screws. (*Figure 6*)

   CAUTION: Make certain line cord wire ends do not touch each other. Check to be sure that wire is routed in plug groove and does not obstruct assembly.

#36 Terminals and Wire Connectors

HOW TO: Connect a wire end to a terminal.

EXPLANATION: In an electrical circuit, any point to which a wire end is connected is called a terminal. Terminals provide a convenient means of connecting electrical parts to their respective wires. In appliances, the most common types of terminals used are the "terminal screw" and the "male terminal spade." Since each terminal secures wire differently, the preparation of the wire ends will depend upon the type of terminal used.

FIG.4

HOOKED WIRE ENDS OF LINE CORD
INSTALLED ON TERMINAL
CONNECTORS

FIG.5

TERMINAL CONNECTORS
INSTALLED IN HALF
OF NEW PLUG

FIG.6   NUTS

PLUG BODY FASTENING SCREWS

Tools and Materials Needed:

      (a) a flatblade screwdriver (medium size)

      (b) a sharp paring knife

      (c) a solderless wire connector (size and type as required) purchased at electrical hardware store

      (d) a crimping tool (for solderless wire connectors), available at local electrical hardware store

      (e) a pair of long-nose pliers

      (f) an emery board

Steps:

1. Prepare the wire end for connection to terminal screw.

    NOTE: A wire may be connected to a terminal screw in one of two ways. In the first, the bare wire end is formed into a hook. The hooked wire end is then placed under the head of the terminal screw. In the second, an appropriate type of solderless terminal connector is first attached to the wire end. The terminal connector is then placed under the terminal screw.

2. To prepare the hooked wire type of connection, first remove about one-half inch of wire covering (insulation) from the wire end. (*Figure 1*) Use a sharp paring knife to cut through the insulation and pull the cut insulation off the wire end. (*Figure 2*)

    CAUTION: When cutting insulation, make certain that copper wire is not nicked or otherwise damaged by knife.

3. If the wire uncovered is solid (one single thick strand of copper), simply form the bare end into a hook with the tip of a pair of long-nose pliers. (*Figure 3*)

FIG.1

PARING KNIFE

WIRE INSULATION

FIG.2

SOLID BARE WIRE

INSULATION REMOVED

FIG.3

FORMING HOOK

LONGNOSE PLIERS

4. If the wire uncovered is stranded (many strands of fine wire) (*Figure 4*), twist the strands together tightly with fingers (*Figure 5*); then form it into a hook with the tip of the long-nose pliers. (*Figure 6*)

5. Place the bare wire hook under the loosened terminal screw, with the hook end facing the direction in which the screw tightens (clockwise). Tighten the terminal screw securely with a screwdriver. (*Figures 7 and 8*)

CAUTION: Do not overtighten terminal screw.

CAUTION: Make sure that none of the wire insulation (covering) gets under the terminal screw to prevent good contact.

CAUTION: Only *one* hooked wire end should be placed under any one terminal screw. If more than one wire is to be connected to a single terminal screw, the wire ends must first be prepared with an appropriate solderless terminal connector. (*Figure 9*) The steps that follow describe the procedures for installing solderless terminal connectors on wire ends for use under terminal screws.

FIG.4

STRANDED TYPE WIRE

FIG.5

WIRE STRANDS TWISTED TOGETHER

FIG.6

STRANDED TYPE WIRE
FORMED INTO HOOK

LONG NOSE PLIERS

FIG.7

TERMINAL SCREW

WIRE

HOOKED
WIRE END

FIG.8

SCREWDRIVER

WIRE

TERMINAL
SCREW

6. Remove about one-half inch of insulation from the wire end. Insert the bare wire end into the wire connector as far as insulation permits. (*Figure 10*)

7. Fasten the wire connector to the wire by placing it halfway into the appropriate size jaw opening of the crimping tool and squeezing the tool handles together hard. (*Figure 11*)

    NOTE: Solderless terminal connectors are made available in many sizes and types. Three important specifications are to be considered when selecting solderless terminal connectors for use with terminal screws. They are: the size (thickness) of the wire on which it is to be installed; the size (thickness) of the terminal screw body onto which it will connect; and the necessary shape of the terminal connector (spade- or ring-shaped). (*Figure 9*) It is always best to take the old (original) terminal connector along with you to the hardware store so that it can be matched with the one to be purchased.

8. When the male terminal spade is used instead of a terminal screw, the wire end must be prepared with a solderless female terminal connector, which may be purchased in any electrical hardware store.

FIG.9   SOLDERLESS TERMINAL CONNECTORS USED WITH TERMINAL SCREWS

SPADE TYPE

RING TYPE

FIG.10

WIRE

BARE WIRE END

FIG.11

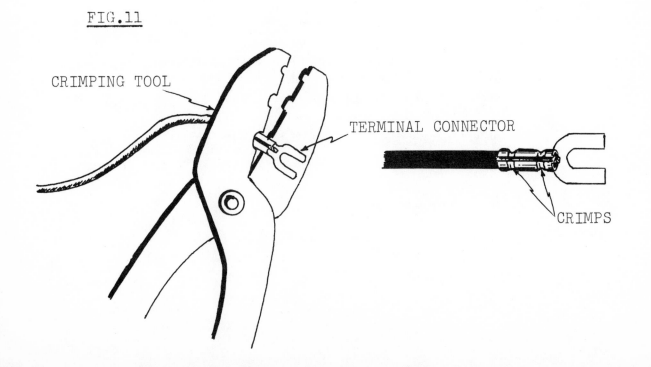

CRIMPING TOOL

TERMINAL CONNECTOR

CRIMPS

9. To prepare the wire end and to install a female terminal connector, refer to steps 6 and 7 for the necessary procedures.

10. Clean the male terminal spade of any dust or dirt by sanding it lightly with an emery board. (*Figure 12*)

11. Connect the female terminal to the male terminal by pushing it on. (*Figure 13*)

#37 Splicing Wires

How To: Join wires with solderless wire connectors.

Explanation: In electrical terms the joining of two or more electric wires is commonly referred to as "splicing." When properly made, a splice produces a wire connection that is a good mechanical bond (wires do not come apart) and a good electrical bond (does not obstruct the flow of electricity). The two splicing techniques described in the following steps can be adapted to cover practically all repair situations that require the joining of wires.

Tools and Materials Needed:

(a) a sharp paring knife

(b) a solderless sleeve connector
(size to correspond with size of the wires to be spliced)

FIG.12

MALE TERMINAL SPADE

FEMALE SPADE
CONNECTOR

TERMINAL CONNECTOR
INSTALLED WITH
CRIMPING TOOL

WIRE

REMOVE DIRT AND RUST

EMERY BOARD

FIG. 13

MALE TERMINAL

FEMALE TERMINAL CONNECTOR

(c) a length of "spaghetti" insulation (pre-formed, sleeve-shaped insulating material available in various diameters and lengths from electrical hardware, electronics, or radio-TV repair stores)

(d) a crimping tool

(e) a wire nut, available from local electrical hardware store (size is determined by the size and number of wires being joined)

(f) a small piece of fine sandpaper (1″ square)

(g) a pair of pliers

STEPS:

1. Select the type of splice which would best meet your repair need. (*Figures 1 and 2*)

   NOTE: The splice shown in *Figure 1* employs a solderless sleeve connector and is used whenever space and the routing of the wires in the appliance demand a continuous, non-bulky splice. The splice shown in *Figure 2* uses a wire nut (simple to install) and can be used whenever space is not a problem or the insulating protection afforded by the wire nut is needed.

2. To complete the splice shown in *Figure 1*, remove a length of insulation (from each wire end) equal to the length of the solderless sleeve connector to be used. Cut the insulation with a sharp paring knife and pull it from the wire ends. (*Figure 3*)

3. Clean the wire ends carefully by wiping them gently with fine sandpaper.

4. Next, cut a piece of spaghetti insulation twice the length of the solderless sleeve connector. Slip the spaghetti insulation onto one of the wires to be spliced. (*Figure 4*)

5. Slip both wire ends (from opposite directions) into the sleeve connector. (*Figure 5*)

FIG.1

SPLICING SLEEVE WITH SPAGHETTI INSULATION
COVERING IN PLACE

FIG.2

WIRE NUT

FIG.3

INSULATION BEING REMOVED

BARE WIRE END

FIG.4

SPAGHETTI INSULATION

BARE WIRE ENDS

FIG.5

SLEEVE CONNECTOR (SPLICING SLEEVE)

6. Fasten the sleeve connector to the wires by placing a crimp in the center of the sleeve connector with the crimping tool. (*Figure 6*)

7. Slide the spaghetti insulation into place over the sleeve connector to complete the splice. (*Figure 1*)

8. To complete the splice shown in *Figure 2,* remove about one-half inch of insulation from each wire end with a paring knife. (*Figure 3*)

9. Clean the wire ends with sandpaper. (*Figure 4*)

10. Cross the wire ends (*Figure 7*) and twist wires together with fingers. (*Figure 8*) Complete the twist to the end of the wires with a pair of pliers. (*Figure 9*)

11. Press wire nut onto wire ends and turn nut clockwise until wire nut is securely attached.

CAUTION: Make certain that the wire nut covers all of twisted wire ends. If not, length of twisted wire ends must be shortened.

SPECIAL NOTE: Wire nuts are made from plastic or porcelain. Plastic wire nuts can be used in situations in which they will not be subjected to extreme heat. Porcelain wire nuts should be used whenever they are to be exposed to high temperatures.

FIG.6

SLEEVE CONNECTOR

CRIMPING TOOL

FIG.7

BARE WIRE ENDS

FIG.8

FIG.9

PLIERS

#38 Insulating Wires

How To: Insulate wire.

Explanation: The material (insulation) used to cover electrical wires acts as a barrier to the flow of electricity. Different materials are used to cover wire. In addition to their electrical insulating qualities, these materials must be capable of withstanding the extreme conditions to which they may be exposed in appliances. These conditions include the presence of oil or grease, high degree of heat, and the presence of excessive moisture. Therefore, whenever it becomes necessary to replace wire insulation, the material used must have the same qualities as that of the original covering.

Tools and Materials Needed:

(a) a pair of scissors

(b) a roll of ½" wide electrical insulating tape (electrical friction tape, electrical plastic tape, or fiberglass tape) selected according to the specific application.

Steps: 1. Determine the type of insulating material required.

NOTE: Electrical friction tape (cloth), electrical plastic tape, and fiberglass tape are three common types of insulating material that are readily available from any electrical hardware store. Moreover, they are easily applied and can fulfill the need for practically every wire repair that requires insulation. Friction tape is a cloth material that contains a black tar-like substance. It can be used for a general repair work as long as it is not exposed to extreme heat or moisture. Plastic tape is a strong elastic type material that is extremely useful whenever a high degree of electrical insulating quality (without bulk) is required. It is also a very effective insulator against moisture. However, it should not be used when it is likely to be exposed to heat. Fiberglass tape, because of its non-inflammable, heatproof characteristics, should be used whenever insulation is required in a condition of extreme heat. All of the insulating tapes discussed above are applied in the same manner and are described in the steps that follow.

2. Begin at a point on the wire about one inch from the bare section to be insulated. (*Figure 1*)

FIG.1

INSULATING TAPE

BARE WIRE

EXISTING WIRE
INSULATION

FIG.2

OVERLAP
WRAPPING

FIG.3

ONE COMPLETED LAYER
OF INSULATION

3. Hold the tape at an angle to the wire and wrap tape around wire. (*Figure 1*)

4. Overlap each turn one-half the width of the tape. (*Figure 2*)

5. Continue wrapping tape for at least one inch past the bare wire section to complete one layer of insulation. (*Figure 3*)

   NOTE: Two layers of insulating tape are generally used for added security, whenever the additional bulk thus created does not interfere with the routing (placement) of the wires.

6. Begin wrapping second layer of insulation from the point at which the first layer ended. (*Figure 4*)

7. Continue wrapping (overlap one-half the width of the tape each turn) back to where the first layer began and cut tape with scissors to complete the second layer. (*Figure 5*)

#39 Mending Heating Elements

How To: Mend broken heating element wire.

Explanation: The practice of mending broken (parted) heating element wire is only a temporary measure. It is intended to restore the operation of an appliance for an emergency need, or when a new replacement element is not available from supply sources. When properly mended, however, the life of heating elements can be extended for many years. Rejoining broken (parted) heating element wire requires the use of fastening devices that can withstand the intense operating heat produced by the element wire. Three methods have proven to be the most effective means of mending element wire. They include the use of a mending sleeve, a nut and bolt, or a blind rivet. The most effective method of the three is the use of the blind rivet because of its tremendous

FIG.4

START OF SECOND LAYER

FIG.5

TWO LAYERS OF INSULATION COMPLETED

SCISSORS

holding power and the fact that it will not become loose. Otherwise, the selection of the type of fastener to be used will depend upon availability and/or the relative ease or difficulty of installation. The steps below describe the procedures for employing each of the three fasteners.

TOOLS AND MATERIALS NEEDED:

All materials and tools listed are available from local electrical hardware stores.

Repair Method Employing Mending Sleeve

(a) a solderless sleeve wire connector

(b) a pair of pliers

Repair Method Employing Nut and Bolt

(a) a #6-32 brass nut and bolt

(b) a pair of long-nose pliers

(c) a flatblade screwdriver (medium size)

Repair Method Employing Blind Rivet

(a) a 1/8″ diameter × 3/16″ grip length steel blind rivet

(b) a back-up washer (1/8″ hole) for use with rivet

(c) a blind riveting tool

STEPS:

1. To rejoin broken element wire with a solderless sleeve connector, straighten approximately one-fourth inch of both wire ends with long-nose pliers. (*Figure 1*)

2. Insert the wire ends into the solderless sleeve connector. (*Figure 2*)

3. Crush the wire connector with a pair of pliers to complete the mend. (*Figure 3*)

4. To rejoin broken element wire with a brass nut and bolt, form both wire ends into loops. (*Figure 4*)

<u>FIG.1</u>

LONGNOSE PLIERS

<u>FIG.2</u>

SLEEVE CONNECTOR

<u>FIG.3</u>

<u>FIG.4</u>

5. Insert bolt through wire loops and thread on the nut. (*Figure 5*)

6. Tighten the nut and bolt securely with a screwdriver and pliers to complete the mend. (*Figure 6*)

7. To rejoin broken heating element wire with a blind rivet, form both ends into loops. (*Figure 4*)

8. Insert rivet mandrel into rivet tool nosepiece. (*Figure 7*)

9. Insert the rivet through the wire loops and place back-up washer on bottom of rivet. (*Figure 8*)

10. Fasten the rivet with the riveting tool. Squeeze the handles of the tool firmly until the rivet mandrel is snapped free of rivet. (*Figure 9*)

11. This completes the mend. (*Figure 10*)

FIG.5 SCREW / NUT

FIG.6 SCREWDRIVER / PLIERS

FIG.7 BLIND RIVETING TOOL / NOSEPIECE / RIVET MANDREL / BLIND RIVET

FIG.8 BLIND RIVETING TOOL / BLIND RIVET / BACK-UP WASHER

FIG.9

FIG.10 RIVETED JOINING

#40 Connecting Heating Elements

How To: Connect heating element wire to a terminal screw.

Explanation: In many appliances, the heating element wires are connected (terminate) directly to a terminal screw. Inspection of an element wire that fails to heat will often
disclose that the end of the element wire has burned
or broken away from a terminal screw. A good heating
element terminal connection must be electrically secure (good conductor of electricity), and it must also
prevent the intense operating heat of the element wire
from reaching and destroying the terminal screw. The
steps below describe a method of reconnecting heating
element wire to a terminal screw that satisfies both
requirements.

Tools and Materials Needed:

(a) a pair of long-nose pliers

(b) a pair of universal pliers

Steps: 1. Remove the terminal nut by unscrewing it from
the terminal screw with the universal pliers. (*Figure 1*)

2. Remove the two metal washers. Make certain that
the broken piece of heating element wire located
between the metal washers is also removed. (*Figure 2*)

3. Inspect the metal washers and terminal nut. If terminal nut and washers appear badly overheated
(blackened or charred), replace them with new
ones.

4. Straighten approximately two inches of the element wire end with the long-nose pliers. (*Figure 3*)

FIG.1

BROKEN HEATING ELEMENT WIRE

FIG.2

MICA
WASHERS

FIG.3

LONGNOSE PLIERS

5. Replace one metal washer on the terminal screw.

6. Wrap the element wire one turn around the terminal screw, allowing at least one inch of the wire to extend out from the screw. (*Figure 4*)

7. Insert the second metal washer onto the terminal screw. (*Figure 5*)

8. Replace the terminal nut and tighten it securely with the universal pliers. (*Figure 6*)

   CAUTION: Do not overtighten terminal nut. Element wire may be crushed and damaged.

9. Twist the end of the element wire extending out from the terminal screw back over the element wire (*Figure 5*) to complete the terminal connection.

#41 Plastic Knobs

How To: Mend a broken plastic appliance control knob.

EXPLANATION: Appliance control knobs crack most often at a point where they grip the metal shafts of switches.

TOOLS AND MATERIALS NEEDED:

(a) a small tube of plastic cement
   (available at hardware stores and children's hobby shops)

(b) a spool of nylon sewing thread

FIG.4

FIG.5

TWIST WIRE BACK

FIG.6

STEPS: 1. Locate small piece of control knob which has been broken off. (*Figure 1*)

2. Carefully apply plastic cement from tube along the edges of the break. (*Figure 2*)

3. Replace the broken piece onto the knob and hold the piece firmly in place until the cement begins to dry (about one minute). (*Figure 3*)

4. Wrap the shaft section of the knob with nylon thread. (*Figure 4*) Make certain thread is pulled tight after each turn. Wind thread as close together as possible.

5. Coat the wound thread with plastic cement. Allow cement to dry thoroughly (about two hours) to complete the mend.

#42 Plastic Parts

How To: Mend cracked or broken plastic appliance parts.

EXPLANATION: The use of plastic materials in the construction of modern appliances is quite extensive. In general, plastic materials have many advantages over some of the metal materials they have replaced. One important advantage is that plastics are good insulators, and when made into appliance parts that are to be handled by the user, they greatly reduce the possibility of electric shock. In normal use, plastic appliance parts can endure as well as most of the previously used metals. Under abnormal conditions, however, such as when an appliance is dropped or struck, plastic components can be cracked or pieces can be broken off.

TOOLS AND MATERIALS NEEDED:

(a) a tube of plastic cement

(b) an epoxy cement kit (transparent)

(c) a small roll of masking tape (¾″ wide)

FIG.1

APPLIANCE KNOB

BROKEN PIECE

FIG.2

CEMENT

FIG.3

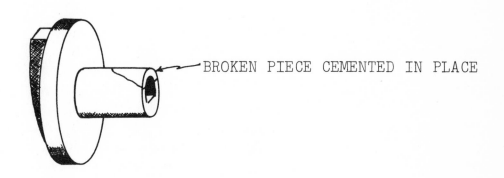

BROKEN PIECE CEMENTED IN PLACE

FIG.4

NYLON THREAD WRAPPING

(d) a sheet of fine (#00) sandpaper

(e) a handful of fine steel wool

(f) a tube of toothpaste

(g) a number of wooden toothpicks

STEPS:

1. Determine the type of cement to be used for the plastic repair.

   NOTE: Many types of plastic materials are used for the construction of appliance components. For mending purposes, however, we shall only determine how the particular type of plastic to be mended will respond to the two commonly used types of cement. For some plastics, plastic cement acts as a solvent and rejoins cracked or broken pieces by actually welding them together. There are other types of plastic materials, however, that are not affected by plastic cement. For these it is best to use an epoxy cement.

2. To pretest the effectiveness of plastic cement, apply a small drop of the cement with a toothpick on a portion of the plastic part that cannot normally be seen.

3. Stir the drop of cement with a toothpick. If the plastic surface is softened (gummy) by the cement, it indicates that the plastic cement will work well. If the plastic remains hard, the epoxy cement will have to be used instead.

4. To mend plastic with plastic cement, first make sure that the pieces to be joined are clean. Wash plastic parts with soap and water to remove any oil or grease. Dry thoroughly.

5. Apply plastic cement sparingly along cracked edges of both broken pieces. (*Figure 1*)

6. Press pieces together firmly and hold them together steadily until cement starts to harden (about one minute).

7. Place a strip of masking tape across (at right angles to) the cemented crack. (*Figure 2*) Pull masking tape taut so that it holds the pieces firmly in place.

FIG.1

BROKEN PLASTIC PART

FIG.2

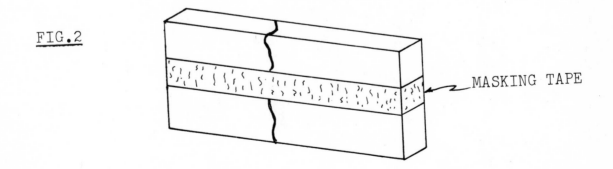

MASKING TAPE

8. Allow plastic cement to dry completely (about two hours). Then remove masking tape. (*Figure 3*)

9. Inspect the mend. If mended crack mars the appearance of the appliance, it may be refinished to improve its appearance.

   NOTE: Besides restoring the finish of mended plastic parts, it may also be desirable at times to remove scratches that accumulate through normal use on the surface of plastic parts and to restore their original luster. This may be accomplished by following steps 10 through 13 as outlined in this section.

10. For mended cracks and deep scratches, first smooth the area by rubbing it *lightly* with a piece of fine sandpaper. (*Figure 4*)

FIG.3

FIG.4

SANDPAPER

11. After all deep scratches have been removed with sandpaper, form a pad with fine steel wool and rub area with steel wool until all fine scratches left by sandpaper are removed. Area should now take on a smooth but hazy appearance. (*Figure 5*)

12. Thoroughly dampen a piece of soft cloth with water. Fold the cloth into a tight pad. (*Figure 6*) Squeeze about one inch of toothpaste onto the cloth and polish plastic area (rub back and forth in straight, even strokes) until luster is obtained.

13. Wipe toothpaste off with soft, clean dry cloth and inspect degree of luster obtained. If it is unsatisfactory, repeat polishing with more toothpaste until finish is satisfactorily restored.

14. To mend plastic components with epoxy cement, first clean plastic with soap and water to remove all dirt, oil, or grease.

15. Prepare an adequate quantity of epoxy cement for the repair at hand. (*Figure 7*)

    NOTE: Epoxy cement is supplied in kits containing two ingredients. These ingredients must be mixed in equal quantities just prior to use. Once the two ingredients are mixed, the hardening process begins.

    CAUTION: Use care and avoid unnecessary contact with epoxy ingredients when working with them. Always follow manufacturer's precautions and instructions.

16. After epoxy cement has been prepared, complete the application of the cement and refinishing of plastic surface (if needed) as outlined in steps 5, 6, and 7. However, be sure to allow epoxy cement 24 hours to set (cure) before removing masking tape or trying to restore plastic finish.

FIG.5

STEEL WOOL

FIG.6

CLOTH PAD

TOOTH PASTE

FIG.7

EPOXY HARDENER

EPOXY RESIN

EQUAL QUANTITIES TO
BE MIXED

GLOSSARY

SMALL FLATBLADE SCREWDRIVER

PHILLIPS TYPE

MEDIUM FLATBLADE SCREWDRIVER

LARGE FLATBLADE SCREWDRIVER

LONG NOSE PLIERS

DIAGONAL CUTTING PLIERS

GLOSSARY

UNIVERSAL PLIERS

CRIMPING TOOL

BLIND RIVETING TOOL

RIVET